GENERALIZING ABOUT NUMBERS

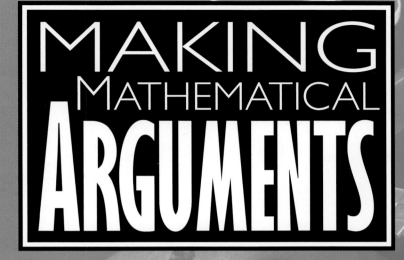

MAKING MATHEMATICAL ARGUMENTS

TEACHER'S GUIDE

D1275903

MathScape™
SEEING AND THINKING MATHEMATICALLY

When Creative Publications was aware of a trademark claim, the designations have been printed in initial capital letters (e.g., Coca-Cola).

Creative Publications and MathScape are trademarks or registered trademarks of Creative Publications.

© 1998 Creative Publications
1300 Villa Street
Mountain View
California 94041

Printed in the United States of America.

0-7622-0220-3
2 3 4 5 6 7 8 9 10. 02 01 00 99 98

Creative Publications

Education Development Center, Inc.

Curriculum Developers for
Making Mathematical Arguments
Susan Janssen, Sue Rasala

EDC Project Director
Glenn M. Kleiman

EDC Core Staff
Amy Brodesky, Rebecca Brown, Dan Brutlag, Kristen Herbert, Susan Janssen, Shelley Isaacson, Andrea Tench, Dan Tobin, Karen Zweig

Other EDC Contributors
Al Cuoco, E. Paul Goldenberg, Marlene Kliman, Leigh Peake, Sue Rasala, Faye Ruopp, Kimberly Smart, Ellen Smith, Marianne Thompson, Albertha Walley, Muffie Wiebe

Additional Contributors
Phyllis Chin, Deanna Wong

Project Collaborators & Consultants
EdMath, Victoria, Australia: Charles Lovitt, Doug Clarke, Ian Lowe

Shell Centre for Mathematical Education, University of Nottingham, England: Hugh Burkhardt, Rosemary Caddy, Malcolm Swan

Inverness Research Associates, Inverness, CA: Barbara Heenan, Mark St. John

Brookline Public Schools, Brookline, MA: Robert Bates

ACKNOWLEDGMENTS

 MathScape Background

The STM project built upon EDC's 40-year history of developing educational materials, including PSSC Physics, ESS Science, The Infinity Factory television series, Insights Science, The Geometric Supposer software series, My Travels with Gulliver, and many other curriculum, software, and video products.

This unit is one of a series of twenty-one MathScape: Seeing and Thinking Mathematically units designed to fully address current standards and recommendations for teaching middle school mathematics. The Seeing and Thinking Mathematically project involved international collaboration with:

- The Shell Centre for Mathematical Education at the University of Nottingham, England, whose contributions built upon many years of research and development underlying materials such as The Language of Functions and Graphs.

- EdMath of Victoria, Australia, whose staff built upon years of research and development producing materials such as the Mathematics Curriculum and Teaching Program (MCTP) materials.

- Inverness Research Associates of California provided consulting on the design of the research processes used in the project and conducted research for several of the units.

The Seeing and Thinking Mathematically project incorporated many formative research activities to assist the developers in designing materials that are mathematically clear and pedagogically effective with diverse populations of students. These activities included summer institutes with middle school teachers, consultations with experts on teaching mathematics to students from different cultural and linguistic backgrounds, reviews of the research on children's learning of mathematics, input from many consultants and advisors, and classroom testing of activities in which the project staff and teachers worked closely together. These research activities helped to define the design principles used throughout the curriculum.

Building from the design principles, initial versions of each unit were then carefully tested in a variety of classrooms, insuring feedback from multiple teachers and diverse groups of students. Project researchers conducted weekly classroom observations and teacher interviews. Student work was collected and analyzed to evaluate the lessons and identify common student misconceptions. The project researchers and curriculum developers used this extensive field test data to revise and improve the units. The field test teachers' classroom experiences and suggestions were also incorporated into the final units in the form of "From the Classroom" notes and "A Teacher Reflects."

This unit of MathScape: Seeing and Thinking Mathematically was developed by the Seeing and Thinking Mathematically project (STM), based at Education Development Center, Inc. (EDC), a non-profit educational research and development organization in Newton, MA. The STM project was supported, in part, by the National Science Foundation Grant No. 9054677. Opinions expressed are those of the authors and not necessarily those of the Foundation.

Field Test Teachers

We wish to extend special thanks the following teachers and their students for their roles in field testing and reviewing units developed by EDC.

ARLINGTON, MA
Carol Martignette Boswell
Steve Porretta

BELMONT, MA
Tony Guarante
Heidi Johnson

BOSTON, MA
Patricia Jorsling
George Perry
Elizabeth Prieto
Bill Rudder

BROOKLINE, MA
Robert Bates
Frank Cabezas
Carolyn Connolly
Arlene Geller-Petrini
Sandra Hegsted
Oakley Hoerth
Judy McCarthy
Carol Mellet
Fran Ostrander
Barbara Scotto
Rhonda Weinstein

Debbie Winkler
Deanna Wong

CAMBRIDGE, MA
Mary Lou Mehring
Jennie Schmidt
Jesse Solomon

FREMONT, CA
Julie Dunkle

INDIO, CA
Lisa Sullivan

LAKEVIEW, CA
Jane Fesler

MILL VALLEY, CA
Patty Armstrong

NEW CANAAN, CT
Sue Kelsey
Bruce Lemoine

NEWTON, MA
Sonya Grodberg
David Lawrence
Mark Rubel

SAN FRANCISCO, CA
Ardreina Gualco
Ingrid Oyen

SOMERVILLE, MA
Jean Foley

SOUTH SAN FRANCISCO, CA
Doug Harik

SUDBURY, MA
Fred Gross
Sondra Hamilton
Jackie Simms

TEMECULA, CA
Ray Segal

TIBURON, CA
Julie Askeland

WALTHAM, MA
Amy Doherty
Diane Krueger
Pat Maloney

We extend our appreciation to Judy Mumme and the following teachers and educators involved in the California Middle School Mathematics Renaissance Project.

Cathy Carroll
SAN MATEO, CA

Deb Clay
HUNTINGTON BEACH, CA

Kathryn Conley
MERCED, CA

Joan Easterday
SANTA ROSA, CA

Linda Fisher
SANTA CRUZ, CA

Marty Hartrick
SAN FRANCISCO, CA

Kevin Jordan
CARMEL, CA

Steve Leliever
LONG BEACH, CA

Carole Maples
WALNUT CREEK, CA

Guillermo Mendieta
AZUSA, CA

Teferi Messert
SACRAMENTO, CA

Mark Rubell
NEWTON, CA

Charles Schindler
RUNNING SPRINGS, CA

Aminah Talib
CARSON, CA

Kevin Truitt
LOS ANGELES, CA

Classroom Testing Teachers

Our thanks to the following classroom teachers for their contributions on the MathScape units.

Heidi Ackley
Steve Ackley
Penelope Jo Black
Bev Brockhoff
Geoff Borroughs
Linda Carmen
Janet Casagrande
Karen Chamberlin
Laura Chan
April Cherrington
Peggy Churchill
Marian Connelly
Jack Cox
Allen Craig
Barbara Creedon
Bill Cummins
Phyllis Cummins
Kathy Duane
Jennifer Dunmire
Karen Edmonds
Sara Effenbeck
Jodie Foster
John Friedrich
Barbara Gneiting
Lisa Gonzales
Ardreina Gualco
Doug Harik
Jennifer Hogerty
Lynn Hoggatt
Ron Johnson
Judy Jones
Sue Lackey
Joan LaComb
Stan Lake
Amanda LaRocca

Claudia Larson
Mona Lasley
Maria Majka
Jim McHugh
Fernando Mendez
Michael Merk
Carol Moore
John Mulkerrins
John Osness
Mary Ann Pella-Donnelly
Charles Perez
Dave Peters
Linda Peters
Lisa Phillips
Jim Pinckard
Ron Rice
Mark Ristow
Thelma Rodriguez
Ellen Ron
Emiliano Sanchez
Wes Schroeder
Janet Schwarz
Cindi Sekera
Doris Selden
Gale Sunderland
Jim Tearpak
Barbara Termaat
Brenda Walker
David Ward
Brenda Watson
Howard Web
Nancy Withers
Hanne Young

Creative Publications Staff and Contributors

Curriculum Director
Linda Charles

MathScape Product Development Team
Ema Arcellana, Katie Azevedo, Bettina Borer, Lynn Clark, Kirstin Cruikshank, Vivien Freund, Janice Gaal, Hyru Gau, Lorraine Groff, Susan Guthrie, Chris Hofer, John Kerwin, Ed Lazar, Heidi Lewis, Joan Marie Lindsay, Lisa Lougee, Mary Scott Martinson, Gregg McGreevy, Andrea Moore, Cherri Nelson, Judith Bao Roubideaux, Lynn Sanchez, Lyn Savage, Vickie Self, Joe Shines, Nancy Steinhardt-Sorensen, Joe Todaro, Miguel Villaseñor, Linda Ward, Sandra Ward, Debra Webster, Stephanie Wooldridge

Credits
Photography: Chris Conroy • Beverley Harper (cover) • Donald Johnson. Illustrations: Gary Taxali • Manfred Geier • Mike Reed • Burton Morris • Susan Williams.

Student Guide Credits:
Photography: Chris Conroy • Beverley Harper (cover) • Donald Johnson. Illustrations: Becky Heavner, pp. 2, 12, 17, 19, 28, 29.

Other Contributors: Amparo del Rio Design • GTS Graphics, Inc. • Manufactured by Banta Book Group.

TABLE OF

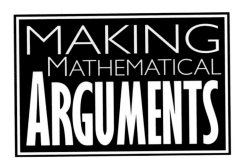

MAKING MATHEMATICAL ARGUMENTS

Generalizing About Numbers

In the investigations in this unit, students learn how to develop sound mathematical arguments by looking for counterexamples and testing special cases. As they proceed, they continually ask themselves this important question: Is it always true?

CONTENTS

THINGS YOU SHOULD KNOW

MathScape™ is a comprehensive three-year middle school mathematics curriculum. *Making Mathematical Arguments* Teacher's Guide contains complete lesson plans, assessment, and reproducible pages. *Making Mathematical Arguments* Student Guide contains lesson pages and homework. MathScape is supported by a *hot* words™, *hot* topics™ handbook for students at each grade level. The handbook contains a glossary, how-to information, and problems for additional homework and practice.

This icon identifies comments that have come from teachers who have used this unit in the classroom. Their experiences and practical suggestions for working through the unit appear in the margin of the Teacher's Guide, next to the teaching steps of each lesson. These **comments from the classroom** may include descriptions of student dialogue, ideas for responding to student misconceptions, varied approaches that address diversity in the classroom, management tips, and suggestions for extending lesson activities.

This icon identifies **notes** of special interest within the teaching steps. These notes often include an indication of what to expect from student writing or discussions. This is also where you will find classroom management tips, information on the rationale behind particular investigations, and some answers.

student page When appropriate, a reduced version of the **Student Guide** page is shown on the Teacher's Guide page for easy reference. The arrow icon is used to indicate which steps on the Teacher's Guide page correspond directly to the steps on the Student Guide page.

The *hot* **words** that appear on the lesson pages in the Student Guide are mathematical terms related to the lesson. The *hot* **topics** appearing in the Teacher's Guide indicate mathematical topics that are recommended for optional review and homework.

If your students have access to the *hot* **words**, *hot* **topics** handbook, they can locate the definitions of the *hot* **words** in the *hot* **words** section of the handbook. You can also direct students to the *hot* **topics** in the handbook, where they will find instruction, examples, and exercises.

If your students do not have the *hot* **words**, *hot* **topics** handbook, you can use *hot* **words** for discussion, referencing them in any mathematical glossary or dictionary. You can use the recommended *hot* **topics** as a guide to help you organize supplemental review materials.

UNIT MATERIALS

The following materials are required for the lessons in *Making Mathematical Arguments*.

PER STUDENT

- calculator

- Rainbow Centimeter Cubes, Fraction Circles, and any other manipulatives that pertain to fractions, such as fraction bars

- Rainbow Centimeter Cubes in two different colors

PER GROUP

- Rainbow Centimeter Cubes

MAKING MATHEMATICAL ARGUMENTS

GENERALIZING ABOUT NUMBERS

All apples are red. Is this a true statement? One counterexample to this statement is "Granny Smith apples are green." A *counterexample* shows that a given statement is not always true. One counterexample is all that is needed to prove that a statement is false.

In this unit, students search for counterexamples as they investigate mathematical statements about adding, subtracting, multiplying, and dividing with signed numbers. Then students use what they have learned to look at patterns that are true for specific cases of numbers, such as whole numbers, and investigate whether those rules can be generalized to include other numbers, such as negative numbers or fractions. Patterns involving square numbers, cubic numbers, prime numbers, and sums of consecutive numbers provide the contexts in which students learn the elements of developing a good mathematical argument.

MAKING MATHEMATICAL ARGUMENTS
AT A GLANCE

PHASE ONE

Signs, Statements, and Counterexamples

By using cubes to model the addition and subtraction of signed numbers, students search for counterexamples to prove that some of the statements they are given about signed number operations are false. As students examine which kinds of equations will result in positive or negative answers, they come to see the meaning behind the algorithms for integer addition and subtraction. Then students move on to investigate multiplication and division of signed numbers. In the final lesson, students pull together what they have learned about signed number operations and about counterexamples.

PHASE TWO

Roots, Rules, and Arguments

The emphasis in Phase Two is on elements of a well-developed mathematical argument. Students begin by using manipulatives to develop a rule about the pattern in the increases of consecutive perfect squares. Then they consider whether the rule should be expanded to include these four special cases: 0, 1, proper fractions, and negative numbers. As students test, analyze, and revise faulty mathematical arguments about squares, square roots, cubes, and cube roots, they develop skills for writing mathematical arguments of their own. Students choose a pattern found in perfect squares as the basis for writing their own mathematical arguments.

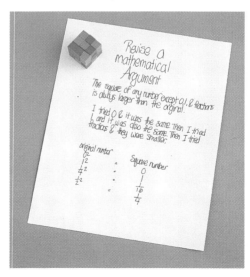

Primes, Patterns, and Generalizations

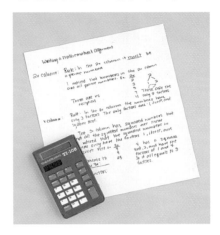

In Phase Three, students become more proficient with writing mathematical arguments. They look for patterns and generalize about their arguments as they explore different areas of number theory, such as divisibility, primes, factors, and multiples. They use manipulatives and create tables to help them discover these patterns more readily. As the major assessment of learning for the unit, students consider patterns involving squares, cubes, primes, factors, and multiples. Then they each select one pattern for which each student develops and refines a mathematical argument of his or her own.

MathScape: *n:* A view of the world from a mathematical perspective.

Math Themes

The theme of **Patterns/Generalizations** is central to the development of mathematical arguments. In the first phase, students are given mathematical statements (generalizations) about operations involving signed numbers and are asked to look for counterexamples as a way of determining whether the statements may be false. In Lesson 1 students begin to come up with rules for predicting the sign of the result when different combinations of positive and negative numbers are added or subtracted. They find out that for some combinations, the results are predictable and a rule can be established. For example, adding a negative number to a negative number will always result in a negative number. Students extend their explorations of rules for signed numbers to include the operations of multiplication and division in subsequent lessons, and eventually come up with a class list of rules for operating with signed numbers, which they have refined based on their explorations with counterexamples.

In the second phase, students test whether statements hold true for whole numbers, proper fractions, signed numbers, and zero and then revise the statements so that they are always true for as many cases of numbers as the rule can apply to. By the end of the third phase, students are ready to identify patterns in a grid array of numbers and use one of the patterns they find as the basis for a mathematical argument of their own.

THE MATHSCAPE

Math Processes

Making and testing conjectures are mathematical processes that are central to this unit. Students begin by testing statements and analyzing arguments that "another student" has made. Students then move on to make conjectures and write statements of their own and to develop their own mathematical arguments to support their statements.

Reasoning is an important part of making a mathematical argument. Logical reasoning is required for conjecturing, testing for counterexamples, and revising statements so that they are always true. The development of students' reasoning skills in this unit is good preparation for later math courses that involve writing and interpretation of "If-then" statements.

Finally, communication is an important aspect of a good mathematical argument. Students gain appreciation for precise language as they see that for a rule statement to be effective it must be worded so that everyone interprets the meaning the same way. Students' communication skills are honed as they first revise existing faulty or inadequate arguments and then go on to devise arguments of their own from scratch. An important part of this process involves making revisions based on classmates' feedback.

Math Strands

Making Mathematical Arguments incorporates the three strands of Number Operations, Geometry/Measurement, and Algebra/Functions.

The first phase serves as a review of rules for adding and subtracting signed numbers and an introduction to rules for multiplying and dividing signed numbers. Students begin by modeling these operations with cubes in their search for examples and counterexamples. By the end of the phase students are expected to be able to perform these operations by following the rules they have investigated, without needing cubes.

In Phase Two, the introduction to square and cubic numbers and their roots begins with visual, geometric representations, which students model with cubes. In Lesson 5, students use cubes or sketches to model geometric patterns of increases in perfect squares, which they relate to their numeric methods for figuring out the increases.

The work with signed number operations, roots, and radicals prepares students for later work with algebra. The type of thinking in which students engage also provides an informal algebraic experience. For example, by examining the pattern in divisibility by 3 of the sum of any three consecutive whole numbers in Lesson 9, students describe in informal language a relationship expressed algebraically as $3n, 3n + 1, 3n + 2$.

NCTM CURRICULUM STANDARDS FOR GRADES 5–8

The standards that correlate to the content in this unit are checked.

✔ Mathematics as Problem Solving

✔ Mathematics as Communication

✔ Mathematics as Reasoning

✔ Mathematical Connections

  Number and Number Relationships

✔ Number Systems and Number Theory

✔ Computation and Estimation

✔ Patterns and Functions

  Algebra

  Statistics

  Probability

  Geometry

  Measurement

PRE-ASSESSMENT

It is helpful if students enter this unit with some experience in the following skills:

- familiarity with operations involving fractions and decimals

- understanding how signed numbers are related to but different from whole numbers

- ability to interpret numbers expressed in exponential form as powers of a number

- experience in identifying and describing patterns

If your students need preliminary work with these skills, you may want to review:

hot words

- signed numbers
- patterns

hot topics

- Multiplication and Division of Fractions
- Powers and Exponents

Have students review the unit overview on pages 2–3 in the Student Guide.

The following question is posed on page 2 of the *Making Mathematical Arguments* Student Guide: What is involved in writing a mathematical argument? This question is investigated in the following pre-assessment activity. Class discussion and individual work will help reveal students' understanding of what numbers belong in the sets of whole numbers and signed numbers, as well as the geometric-array interpretation of multiplication.

Materials

Per pair:

- 16 Rainbow Centimeter Cubes

Prerequisite Check

In this unit, students will test mathematical statements to see if they are always true. This involves looking at special cases such as 0, 1, negative numbers, and fractions. To review and check what students know about special cases, ask these questions:

- What kinds of numbers have you worked with in math?
- What are signed numbers? What are some examples of signed numbers?
- What are whole numbers? (Answer: Any number in the set {0, 1, 2, 3, 4, 5, ...})
- When you multiply with whole numbers, how are the terms *factor* and *product* used?

Performance Task

Distribute the cubes to students. On an overhead projector, make a 2×8 rectangle of cubes. Discuss with students how this shape represents a multiplication problem.

Discuss how 2 and 8 are factors of 16. Ask students to use cubes to find the different rectangles (or squares) possible with 16 cubes. Have them draw each rectangle and label the length and width with the number of cubes. Then ask students to write responses to these questions:

- How do you know you found all the possible rectangles? Make up and describe a system for keeping track of the rectangles so that you know you found them all.
- Describe your system so that it works for *any* number of cubes. Choose other numbers, such as 21, 24, or 30. Draw rectangles for them.
- How can you use the rectangles to find all the factors of a number? How do you know when you have found them all?

On the board write 4^2. Discuss these questions:

- How do you read this number? What does it mean?
- What do we call the 2?
- How could you show 4^2 with cubes?

Ask students to try to describe a procedure that tells how to determine when all the factors of a number have been found.

See Pre-assessment page A4 for assessment information and sample student work.

PLANNING AND PACING

A Typical Path Through the Unit

Typically this unit takes approximately 25 class periods, each lasting 45 minutes. You can use a copy of the Assessment Checklist, Reproducible R1, as a planning tool to record the days you will spend on each lesson. As you plan for this unit, you will want to keep in mind that a typical lesson takes two days. The amount of time you spend on a lesson may be influenced by the demands of your particular class.

I felt my class needed to spend more time on signed number operations. I extended the time we spent in Phase One by two days and made up for the time by cutting Lessons 8, 9, 11, and 12. I used Lesson 10 as the final assessment.
Phase One: Allow 2 extra days to work more with signed number operations.
Phase Two: Cut Lesson 8.
Phase Three: Cut Lessons 9, 11, and 12.
Time: 19 class sessions ☐

I had fewer than 25 class days to allow for the unit, but wanted my students to get to the final assessment activity. I used all of Phase One, but in Phase Two I skipped Lessons 7 and 8 involving cubic numbers and other powers greater than 2. My students were able to complete all the lessons in Phase Three, although in Lessons 11 and 12 they weren't able to look for patterns involving cubic numbers.
Phase One: Remains as is.
Phase Two: Cut Lessons 7 and 8.
Phase Three: Remains as is, except that students do not find patterns involving cubic numbers.
Time: 21 class sessions ☐

Making Mathematical Arguments ASSESSMENT CHECKLIST

Name: ___   Period: ___   Date: ___

Lesson	Assignment Description	Assessment	Notes
			Day 1
Pre-assessment	What is involved in writing a mathematical argument?		Days 2-3
Lesson 1	Statements About Signs		Days 4-5
Lesson 2	Counterexamples and Cube Combinations		Days 6-7
Lesson 3	More Cases to Consider		Days 8-9
Lesson 4	Rules to Operate By		
Phase One Skill Check	Skill Quiz 1 & Homework 1–4		Days 10-11
Lesson 5	Perfect Pattern Predictions		Days 12-13
Lesson 6	Counterexamples and Special Cases		Days 14-15
Lesson 7	Root Relationships		Days 16-17
Lesson 8	A Powerful Argument		
Phase Two Skill Check	Skill Quiz 2 & Homework 5–8		Days 18-19
Lesson 9	Three-Stack Shape Sums		Days 20-21
Lesson 10	A Stretching Problem		Days 22-23
Lesson 11	Pattern Appearances		Days 24-25
Lesson 12	The Final Arguments		
Phase Three Skill Check	Skill Quiz 3 & Homework 9–12		
Post-assessment	What is involved in writing a mathematical argument?		

Comments:

CURRICULUM LINKS

This unit can be the focus of an interdisciplinary unit on the different aspects of proof in history, law, and science. The following books and materials will help students examine the differences between debate, scientific argument, and mathematical argument.

How to Debate

By Robert Dunbar

Part of the *Speak Out, Write On!* series, this book offers a simple guide to debating. A more advanced CNN video series (1-800-266-6397), *Debate I, II and III* introduces students to inductive and deductive reasoning, error analysis, and formal debate.

To Kill a Mockingbird

By Harper Lee

This classic novel tells the story of a white lawyer from a small town who defends an innocent black man accused of rape. The lawyer's compassionate, yet doomed arguments alienate him from the community, but earn him the respect of his two children.

The Great Monkey Trial

By Tom McGowan

This book discusses the outcomes and implications for continuing debate between evolutionists and creationists. Also good is the play *Inherit the Wind*, by Jerome Lawrence, which dramatizes this courtroom battle.

Life Story

Sunburst

This multimedia CD-ROM presents an annotated movie that becomes the common thread that describes "The Race for the Double Helix." Students view film clips and on-screen text to develop a fuller understanding of how scientists investigate a hypothesis and defend their findings (1-800-321-7511).

ETs and UFOs: Are They Real?

By Larry Kettelkamp

An overview of reported sightings of UFO reports, as well as the agencies whose work it is to monitor and investigate such claims. Also good for debate is *UFOs : Opposing Viewpoints*, by Michael Arvey.

Other Resources

The MegaMath project (http://www.c3.lanl.gov/mega-math/) contains five dynamic mathematical simulations. In *A Usual Day at Unusual School*, students perform a play which takes place in a school where some of the students always lie and the rest always tell the truth. Students must use logic to uncover the truth.

KEY WORDS

The following words can be used in combination or singly as starting points for students who wish to further explore the concepts presented in this unit:

- **proof**
- **debate**
- **investigate**
- **fact and opinion**
- **critical thinking**

Signs, Statements, and Counterexamples

Using cubes to model problems with signed numbers, students search for counterexamples to determine whether they can show that statements about signed number operations are false.

Create Statements and Counter Examples
1. A positive plus another positive will equal a negative.
2. A positive minus a negative equals a negative.
3. A positive multiplied by a negative equals a positive.
4. A negative divided by a positive equals a positive.
5. A positive plus a positive equals positive.
6. A negative subtract a negative equals negative or positive.
7. A positive × a negative equals negative.
8. A positive ÷ a negative equals negative.

Answer Key
1. (False) 2 + 2 = 4

Statements About Signs

To begin their exploration of rules for signed number operations, students use cubes to model adding and subtracting signed numbers. They begin to create and model solutions to their own individual problems. Students use this technique of modeling with cubes to search for counterexamples. In this way they learn to determine whether statements they are given are always true.

Mathematical Goals

- Use manipulatives to calculate integer addition and subtraction problems.

- Create integer problems that fit certain mathematical criteria.

- Find and define counterexamples to a mathematical statement.

- Understand the role of a counterexample in negating a mathematical statement.

MATERIALS

PER STUDENT

- 10 Rainbow Centimeter Cubes in two different colors (5 of each color)

- Reproducible R8

PREPARATION

Be sure to review the Math Background on pages 12–13 before beginning this lesson.

Counterexamples and Cube Combinations

Students continue working with cubes to create different addition and subtraction problems within particular mathematical constraints. They then examine which kinds of equations will result in positive or negative answers, and the class creates a chart summarizing their findings. Through this activity, students begin to internalize how the addition and subtraction algorithms work with signed numbers.

MATERIALS

PER STUDENT

- 10 Rainbow Centimeter Cubes in two different colors (5 of each color)

- Reproducible R9

(Optional: Subtraction Puzzles is an optional assignment designed for students to work on when they have extra time.)

Mathematical Goals

- Perform addition and subtraction with integers.

- Understand how different combinations of positive and negative integers can be added or subtracted to get a particular result.

- Begin to think about the mathematical boundaries for the domain and range of different problems.

- Look for counterexamples to a rule.

LESSON 3

More Cases
to Consider

Students use cubes to model examples of multiplication problems and show the four combinations of positive and negative numbers possible (P × P, P × N, N × P, N × N). This makes the rules which they learn for multiplication of signed numbers more meaningful. Then students use what they know about the relationship between multiplication and division to investigate division of signed numbers. At the end of the lesson, students apply their understanding of signed number operations to create statements that are always true and statements that have counterexamples.

Mathematical Goals

- Perform multiplication with integers.

- Use manipulatives and apply understanding of the relationship between multiplication and division to calculate division problems.

- Apply understanding of counterexamples to state rules about integer operations.

MATERIALS

PER STUDENT

- 10 Rainbow Centimeter Cubes in two different colors (5 of each color)

PREPARATION

Make a transparency of Multiplication with Signed Numbers, Reproducible R10. Have an overhead projector and transparency pens available. Make sure students have their solutions to the statements from Lesson 1.

LESSON 4

Rules to
Operate By

The last lesson of Phase One pulls together what students have learned about signed number operations and counterexamples and serves as an assessment for the phase. Students consider operations that are equivalent and look for counterexamples to determine whether statements about addition and subtraction are always true. Finally, they write a general rule for multiplying and dividing with integers.

Mathematical Goals

- Understand that subtracting a negative is equivalent to adding a positive, and that subtracting a positive is equivalent to adding a negative.

- Find counterexamples to statements about signed number operations.

- Find a general rule for multiplication and division problems that will determine when answers will be positive and when answers will be negative.

MATERIALS

PER STUDENT

- calculator

PREPARATION

In Step 3 of this lesson, you may want to use some of the statements that students created in Lesson 3, Step 4. You may either add to or replace the statements in Is It Always True? on Student Guide page 13.

MATH BACKGROUND

Beginning in Lesson 1, students learn how to add and subtract signed numbers using cubes. The use of manipulatives to model specific signed number problems allows students to verify answers in a concrete way. In this unit, students are asked to use pink cubes to represent positive integers and green cubes to represent negative integers.

Adding with the Same Sign

Addition problems involving same-sign numbers are the most straightforward to represent. For example, the problem $-3 + (-2)$ is shown here. Three negative cubes are laid out first, then two negative cubes are added to the pile. The sign of the result, -5, is clear.

Adding with Different Signs

In addition problems where the signs of the numbers are different, pairs of cubes that equal 0 are removed to find the solution. The problem $4 + (-2)$ is shown here.

4 positive cubes are laid out and 2 negative cubes are added in.

Pairs of positive and negative cubes are removed.

The cubes left indicate the number and sign of the result, $+2$.

Subtracting Without Zero-Pairs

Some subtraction problems are also quite straightforward, such as $-3 - (-1)$.

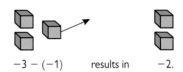

$-3 - (-1)$ results in -2.

Subtracting with Zero-Pairs

However, other subtraction problems may involve adding zero-pairs in order to model the subtraction. The problem $2 - (-3)$ is shown here.

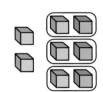

2 positive cubes are laid out.

In order to have 3 negative cubes to subtract, 3 zero-pairs are added. The additional zero-pairs do not change the value of the number.

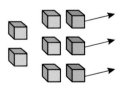

The 3 negative cubes are taken away, leaving 5 positive cubes.

In this example, 3 negative cubes were needed to model the calculation, so 3 zero-pairs were added. It is not necessary for students to add the exact number of zero-pairs needed, since any additional zero-pairs will simply cancel out, as shown in the problem $-3 - 1$.

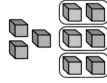

3 negative cubes are laid out.

In order to have $+1$ to subtract, some zero-pairs are added.

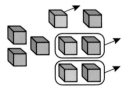

Then $+1$ is subtracted, as well as the additional zero-pairs.

The result is -4.

I reviewed signed numbers by drawing a number line on the chalkboard with zero in the center and labeling it to show integers from 0 to 5 and from 0 to −5. To explain what a zero-pair is, such as (2, −2), I started at 0 and moved forward to 2, and then back to −2. □

I tried the lesson out in two different classes and initially used the handout Cube Calculations with Signed Numbers on the overhead, but decided it was too much of a challenge for my second-language learners to get past the words. In the second class I wrote on an overhead in different colors, and these students in that class seemed to have an easier time picking up the new concepts correctly, needing less repetition. □

Statements About Signs

Have students review the phase overview on pages 4–5 in the Student Guide.

1 Representing Positive and Negative Numbers with Cubes

Distribute 10 cubes of two different colors (5 of each color) to each student. Establish which color will represent positive numbers and which will represent negative numbers with the class. After reviewing an example of how pairs of opposite numbers added together equal 0 (such as 2 and −2), show students how to model this example with the cubes. Distribute Cube Calculations with Signed Numbers, Reproducible R8, and discuss the different ways to show the number 5 drawn on the top portion of the sheet.

> Help students understand that zero-pairs do not change the numerical value of a representation. Any number of zero-pairs can be added or removed without changing the quality represented. Adding or taking away pairs of cubes that cancel out to 0 is an important part of the addition and subtraction algorithms students will learn in this lesson.

2 Using Cubes to Model Calculations

student page

Discuss the examples shown on the bottom portion of Cube Calculations with Signed Numbers with the class. You might want students to model the examples with their cubes. The use of cubes to model these operations gives students a visual model that they eventually internalize. As they

become more familiar with modeling equations, making calculations with signed numbers and determining the sign of the results becomes automatic.

> One goal of the investigation is to teach students a concrete algorithm for solving simple signed number problems. As students become more familiar with the algorithm in later lessons, they will be able to visualize the model without needing the cubes. Also try to have students figure out how to use the cubes to solve different kinds of problems. This way students do not need to know how to do every possible kind of example before they begin. See Assessment page A26 for solutions.

3 Thinking About Counterexamples

Tell students that two students, Hyun and Tanya, were working on the cube investigation together as partners. Hyun noticed two problems in which a negative number was added to a positive number, resulting in a positive number: $6 + (−3)$ and $−4 + 7$. Hyun pointed this out to Tanya, but Tanya was not convinced this would always be true and started looking for a counterexample. Hyun did some quick calculations and showed Tanya five more problems in which this was true. Ask students to think about whether they agree with Hyun or Tanya.

Student work shown on the following pages is provided as a guide only and is not intended as an answer key.

LESSON HOMEWORK

Making Mathematical Arguments
Student Guide page 34
Solutions: Assessment page A29

hot topics

- *Counterexamples*

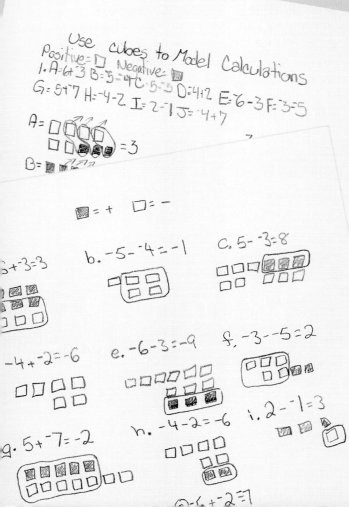

Use cubes to Model Calculations
Positive = □   Negative = ■
1. A = 6 + 3 B = 5 - 4 C = 5 - 3 D = 4 + 2 E = 6 - 3 F = 3 - 5
G = 5 + 7 H = -4 - 2 I = 2 - 1 J = -4 + 7

A = □□□□□□ = 3

B =

■ = +   □ = -

b. -5 - 4 = -1   c. 5 - 3 = 8

a. 6 + 3 = 3

-4 + 2 = -6   e. -6 - 3 = -9   f. -3 - 5 = 2

g. 5 + 7 = -2   h. -4 - 2 = -6   i. 2 - 1 = 3

---

1 Statements About Signs

EXPLORING
INTEGER
STATEMENTS WITH
COUNTEREXAMPLES

You know the rules for adding and subtracting whole numbers so well that you hardly have to stop and think about them. In this lesson, you will use examples and counterexamples to explore statements about adding and subtracting with signed numbers.

Use Cubes to Model Calculations

How could you use cubes to model adding and subtracting positive and negative numbers?

Using cubes can help you get a better sense of how to calculate problems with positive and negative numbers. After the class discusses the handout Cube Calculations with Signed Numbers, complete the following:

1 On your paper, write each of the Signed Number Problems shown. Use cubes to figure out the solution. Then write the solution.

2 Make up a problem in which you need to add zero-pairs to your cubes to solve it. Start with 5 cubes. Illustrate your problem with cubes.

3 Make up a problem in which you need to add some negative cubes to solve it. Illustrate your problem with cubes.

Signed Number Problems

1. $6 + (-3)$	**2.** $-5 - (-4)$	**3.** $5 - (-3)$	**4.** $-4 + (-2)$
5. $-6 - 3$	**6.** $-3 - (-5)$	**7.** $5 + (-7)$	**8.** $-4 - 2$
9. $2 - (-1)$	**10.** $-4 + 7$		

I asked the students if they thought the statement "all apples are red" was always true. I continued with these questions: Is this statement a rule? Why or why not? What makes something a rule? Then I told them that a counterexample is an example that shows a statement can be untrue. We then talked about how many counterexamples you need to find to show that a statement is not a rule. □

One student was helpful in explaining to others that in an addition problem, "If it's more negative, the answer is negative." She was referring to this problem that she created: $3 + (-6) = -3$. Then she noted, "If it's more positive, it's positive," using this example: $-3 + 6 = 3$. □

4 Discussing a Counterexample

Use the vignette from Step 3 as the basis for a class discussion to introduce the concept of a counterexample. Students may encounter statements for which there are many supporting examples and no readily apparent counterexamples. In Step 3, Hyun was convinced that a negative number and a positive number would always have a positive sum. Before students determine that a statement is true, it is important that they use the resources available, such as positive and negative number cubes, to develop a persuasive argument that no counterexample could possibly exist. Ask students the following questions.

- Do you think Hyun's statement is always true? Why?

- How many more examples should Hyun find in order to make a good argument?

- How many counterexamples would Tanya need to find to show that Hyun's rule does not work?

Both in mathematics and in everyday life, a statement that is proposed to be universally true may use the words *all, every,* or *always;* for instance, "All birds can fly." There may be many examples that support the statement; in this instance, we know that robins can fly, eagles can fly, and so on. However, an ostrich is a bird that cannot fly—a counterexample for the statement proposed about all birds. The statement is false as given; however, it may be revised into a true statement by changing the word *all* to *many.*

5 Looking for Counterexamples

After students have read over the set of mathematical statements written by Hyun and Tanya, ask them to identify those statements that are always true and those that have counterexamples. Make sure students save their work to use in Lesson 3. See Assessment page A26 for solutions.

6 Comparing and Discussing Statements

Arrange students in small groups and have them compare their solutions to the different statements from Hyun and Tanya. You may want to remind students that even though Hyun and Tanya sometimes give an example that works, they should look for a possible counterexample. Let students know that they should be prepared to explain and justify their responses in the class discussion which will follow. This will help to reinforce the concept of counterexamples for students.

what to look for

DOES STUDENT WORK SHOW AN UNDERSTANDING OF:

- *how to use manipulatives to model addition and subtraction with integers?*
- *what a counterexample is?*
- *how to use a counterexample to negate a mathematical statement?*

See *Making Mathematical Arguments* **Assessment page A5 for assessment information.**

Look for Counterexamples

For each statement below, decide if the statement will always be true. If the statement is not always true, show an example for which it is false (a *counterexample*). If the statement is always true, present an argument to convince others that no counterexamples can exist.

> **How can you argue that a mathematical statement is always true, or show that it is not always true?**

1. I tried four different problems in which I added a negative number and a positive number, and each time the answer was negative. So a positive plus a negative is always negative. — Hyun

2. I noticed that a negative number minus a positive number will always be negative, because the subtraction makes the answer even more negative. — Tanya

3. I think that a negative number minus another negative number will be negative. because with all those minus signs, it must get really negative. — Hyun

4. A negative decimal number + a positive decimal number will equal 0 because they will cancel out. One example of this is −0.25 + 0.25. — Tanya

5. A positive fraction, like $3/4$, minus a negative fraction, like $−1/2$ will always give you an answer that is more than 1. — Hyun

6. A negative decimal + a negative decimal will always give you a negative answer. — Tanya

7. You never need to add zero-pairs to your cubes when doing an addition problem — Hyun

hot **words** | signed numbers
counterexample

Homework
page 34

MAKING MATHEMATICAL ARGUMENTS   LESSON 1
© Creative Publications • MathScape   **7**

Predicting Results of Integer Addition and Subtraction

My students needed help coming up with a systematic way to make sure they had found all the different possible problems for each question. So I helped them think about starting with all negative cubes, gradually including more positive cubes in their starting numbers until they start with all positive cubes. I used the first sample problem as an example, where the first solution starts with 5 negatives cubes. The next solution started with 4 negatives and 1 positive, then 3 negatives and 2 positives, then 2 negatives and 3 positives, and so on. □

Counterexamples and Cube Combinations

1 Solving Sample Problems

Distribute 5 cubes each of two different colors to each student. Have students work individually to create equations for the descriptions below. Keep a list of the different equations that students suggest.

a. Use 5 negative cubes to make up a problem for which the answer is −2.

b. Use 1 negative cube and 4 positive cubes. Remove any zero-pairs. Use the remaining cubes to make up a problem for which the answer is −2. You may add other cubes to get your answer.

c. Start with other combinations of 5 cubes. Remove any zero-pairs. Then add or subtract cubes to create a problem for which the answer is −2.

> Notice that in every case the starting number of cubes is fixed at 5 and the answer to each problem is fixed at −2. This prepares students for the next step, where they will use the cubes to generate their own signed number problems that fit particular mathematical constraints. See Assessment page A27 for solutions.

2 Using Cubes to Create Equations

student page

Check on students as they think of different problems individually or in pairs. Some students may need help coming up with appropriate combinations of cubes for each problem. Each of the problems in this investigation asks students to find all the possible values that a fixed number of cubes can represent. Then students add or remove cubes to yield particular results, and write the related equations. If some students finish early, suggest that they work on Subtraction Puzzles, Reproducible R9. These puzzles complement the problems in this step well, since the problems involve more addition than subtraction. Encourage students to use the subtraction algorithms with cubes that they learned in Lesson 1.

> The goal of this investigation is to give students more experience with addition and subtraction of signed numbers and to have students solve problems that require algebraic thinking. As students generate the different problems, they are, in effect doing problems of the form "some number $\pm N = -2$" even though they are not using variables. This is an example of early algebraic thinking. See Assessment page A27 for solutions.

LESSON HOMEWORK

Making Mathematical Arguments

Student Guide page 35
Solutions: Assessment page A30

hot
topics

• *Addition and Subtraction of Fractions*

① $-5--3=-2$

② $+3-+5=-2$
$+3-+-5=-2$

③ ⊞⊞⊞ ⟩ +1
⊟

$+1-+3=-2$
$+1+-3=-2$ ⟩ -1

$-1-+1=-2$
$-1+-1=-2$

⟩ -3

$-3--1=-2$
$-3++1=-2$

---

2 Counterexamples and Cube Combinations

PREDICTING
RESULTS OF
INTEGER ADDITION
AND SUBTRACTION

In the last lesson, you explored statements about the results of adding and subtracting with signed numbers. In this lesson, you will analyze equations you create yourself. This will help you make predictions about whether the result of an equation will be positive or negative.

Use Cubes to Create Equations

How can you use cubes to create signed number problems when you know what the answer is?

The value represented by a given number of cubes depends on how many of the cubes are positive and how many are negative. In the following problems, build representations with cubes, and then record each equation in writing.

1 Make all possible combinations of 3 cubes. For each combination, bring in additional cubes so that the overall total is -4.

2 Make all possible combinations of 4 cubes. For each combination, remove cubes or bring in additional cubes so that the overall total is -1.

3 Make all possible combinations of 5 cubes. For each combination, remove cubes or bring in additional cubes so that the overall total is -1.

Signed Number Problem

Start with 6 negative cubes. Show a problem with the cubes for which the answer is -3.

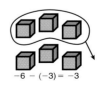

$-6 - (-3) = -3$

My students needed more guidance and modeling with choosing equations from the class chart of combinations. We brainstormed examples as a class before students wrote their own examples. This helped students develop some confidence in learning to "cite" examples. □

3 Sorting the Solutions

After students have written all possible combinations, stop the class and help them generate a chart of all the combinations for adding and subtracting signed numbers like the chart shown on the opposite page. Have students sort the equations that they wrote in Step 2 into categories on the class chart. This will help students see whether a type of equation always has a positive result or a negative result, or can have either type of result. Remind students to compare answers with one another to see if they have found all possible solutions, and to see if they have made any computation mistakes.

4 Predicting a Positive or Negative Answer

Create an answer chart with the class as shown on the opposite page, but do not fill in the answers. Use the questions below to help students think about which combinations of signed numbers will always be positive or negative. Encourage students to look for counterexamples to any of the rules they come up with. This will reinforce looking for counterexamples as part of the process of establishing a rule, and will help students describe the rules in more general terms.

- Which kinds of equations will always result in a positive answer? in a negative answer?

- Can you find any counterexamples to any of the rules we have come up with?

- A negative minus a negative can be negative, positive, or zero. When will the result be positive? negative? zero?

Some combinations can always be predicted, whereas others depend on the numbers added or subtracted. As students think about how to predict the sign of the result, they think more abstractly about the rules for addition and subtraction of signed numbers. The goal of this discussion is not to establish rules for students to memorize, but rather to help students move from the physical cubes to visualizing the process and thinking about the range of numbers for which different results will be positive or negative. This foreshadows Phase Two, in which students learn to think about the mathematical boundaries of a problem as they develop a mathematical argument.

5 Explaining the Results

As students write paragraphs about their results, they use their own words to describe the results of the discussion from the previous step. You can have students share their writing with the class to further reinforce understanding of positive and negative numbers and counterexamples.

what to look for

DOES STUDENT WORK SHOW AN UNDERSTANDING OF:

- *how to use manipulatives to model problems with mathematical boundaries?*
- *the different combinations of positive and negative numbers possible?*
- *rules for addition and subtraction of positive and negative numbers?*
- *finding counterexamples to a rule?*

See *Making Mathematical Arguments* Assessment page A5 for assessment information.

ANSWER CHART

Positive + Positive = Positive

Positive + Negative = Positive, Negative, or Zero

Negative + Positive = Positive, Negative, or Zero

Negative + Negative = Negative

Positive − Positive = Positive, Negative, or Zero

Positive − Negative = Positive

Negative − Positive = Negative

Negative − Negative = Positive, Negative, or Zero

Sort the Solutions

Investigate the questions below about the results of adding and subtracting signed numbers. As you investigate, keep in mind that important question: Is it always true?

When can you predict whether an answer will be positive or negative?

1 What are the possible combinations of positive and negative numbers in an addition or subtraction equation that involves just two numbers? Be ready to share all the combinations you can think of with the class. The class will make a chart of all the combinations.

2 Look at the class chart of combinations.

   a. For which combinations on the chart can the sign of the result always be predicted?

   b. For which combinations on the chart does the sign of the result depend on the particular numbers in the equation?

Remember to look for counterexamples if you think you have found a rule.

Explain the Results

Choose one kind of combination from the class chart that will always have a negative answer. Choose another kind of equation from the class chart of combinations where the sign of the answer depends on the numbers being added or subtracted.

For both kinds of equations, write one paragraph that explains the following:

- Will the result always be positive or negative? Why?

- If it depends, what does it depend on?

hot **words**   signed numbers equation

 H**o**mework

page 35

More Cases to Consider

Exploring Integer Multiplication and Division

Some of my students were not familiar with the commutative property of multiplication. They were still unsure that reversing the order of the factors in a multiplication problem yields the same result. To help them understand the commutative property, I had them use cubes to model some examples with whole numbers such as 3 × 4 and 4 × 3. □

student page

1 Using Cubes to Model Multiplication

Begin by reviewing what students already know about multiplication of whole numbers. As an example, discuss how 2 × 3 can be shown as 2 groups of 3. Distribute the cubes and ask students to model this with their cubes. Remind them that when they think about multiplication problems, they can think of the first number as telling how many groups and the second number as telling how many things are in each group. When you are sure students have a good understanding of this way of modeling multiplication, have them begin the investigation.

There are four possible combinations of products of signed numbers: P × P, P × N, N × P, N × N. Since these are the same combinations they found for addition and subtraction in the last lesson, students should have no difficulty listing them in this step. Only the first two cases can be modeled with cubes, since there is no way to model a "negative group." Rather than tell students this from the outset, it is worthwhile having them discover the problem themselves. You may want to let students know that they may not be able to model all the combinations.

2 Establishing the Rules for Multiplication of Signed Numbers

Discuss the results students came up with in their attempts to model examples of the different combinations of two signed number factors.

- What were the four combinations you listed?

- What were the sample problems you wrote for each combination?

- Which problems were you able to model with cubes? What results did you get?

- Can you think of any ways to solve the problems you were not able to model with cubes?

Display the transparency Multiplication with Signed Numbers, Reproducible R10. For each case, discuss the sample problem and establish the rule with the students. The approach to Case 3, in which N × P is considered to be the same as P × N, involves understanding of the commutative property of multiplication. Case 4, the product of two negative numbers, invites class discussion.

LESSON HOMEWORK

Making Mathematical Arguments
Student Guide page 36
Solutions: Assessment page A31

hot topics

- *Integer Operations*
- *Counterexamples*

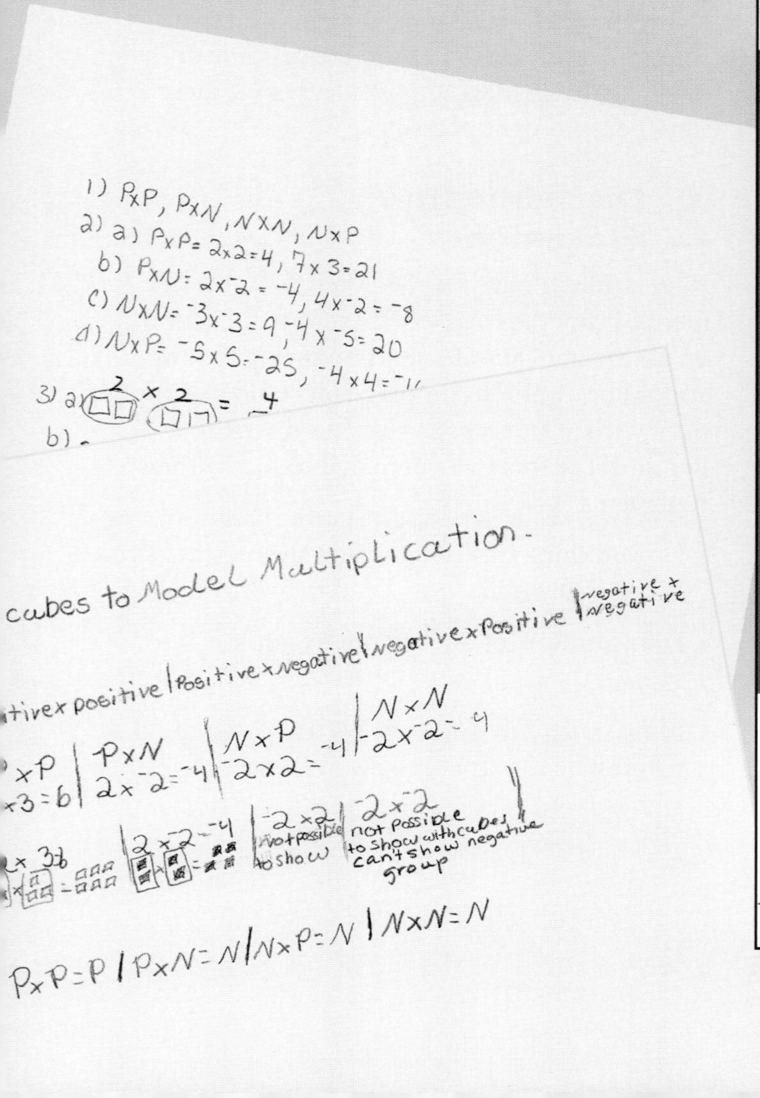

[Handwritten notes on worksheet:]

1) $P \times P$, $P \times N$, $N \times N$, $N \times P$

2) a) $P \times P = 2 \times 2 = 4$, $7 \times 3 = 21$

b) $P \times N = 2 \times^- 2 = ^-4$, $4 \times^- 2 = ^-8$

c) $N \times N = ^-3 \times^- 3 = 9$, $^-4 \times^- 5 = 20$

d) $N \times P = ^-5 \times 5 = ^-25$, $^-4 \times 4 = ^-16$

3) a) $2 \times 2 = ^-4$

b)

cubes to Model Multiplication.

negative × positive	Positive × negative	negative × Positive	negative × negative
$\times P$ $\times 3 = 6$	$P \times N$ $2 \times^- 2 = ^-4$	$N \times P$ $^-2 \times 2 = ^-4$	$N \times N$ $^-2 \times^- 2 = 4$
$\times 3 = 6$	$2 \times^- 2 = ^-4$	$^-2 \times 2 = ^-4$ not possible to show	$^-2 \times^- 2$ not possible to show with cubes can't show negative group

$P \times P = P$ | $P \times N = N$ | $N \times P = N$ | $N \times N = N$

---

3 More Cases to Consider

EXPLORING
INTEGER
MULTIPLICATION
AND DIVISION

Now that you have learned how to add and subtract signed numbers, it is time to move on to multiplication and division. After finding the rules for multiplication, you will investigate rules for division. Then you will be ready to write your own statements and counterexamples to summarize what you have learned so far about signed numbers.

Use Cubes to Model Multiplication

How can you use cubes to model multiplication of signed numbers?

You have used cubes to model adding and subtracting with two numbers and made a chart of the results. Can you find ways to use cubes to model multiplying different combinations of signed numbers?

$$2 \times (-3)$$

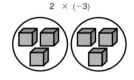

1 List all the different combinations of two signed numbers that could be multiplied.

2 For each combination you listed, write down some sample problems.

3 Try to find a way to use cubes to model examples of a multiplication problem for each combination of two numbers. Draw pictures of your models to record your work.

4 Write down any conclusions you can make about the results when multiplying each combination.

Students were successful with creating statements and counterexamples. For the ESL students, we created one example for each and then they continued on their own. These students needed this additional modeling to insure they understood what was expected of them. They were more secure having an example, so I seldom heard, "Is this right?" □

I passed a pair of students who were talking about the movie Living in Color. *They called me over and explained, "There is a part in the movie where the math teacher is doing this kind of math and the kids are in high school. Remember how the teacher kept saying that TWO of the same signs get you a positive?" Not only did these students relate their outside activities to the topic, they also showed me another way to visualize the multiplication and division of signed numbers.* □

3 Investigating Division of Signed Numbers

Ask students how they think the rules for division will work. For the problems students are not able to model with cubes, encourage students to think about division as the inverse of multiplication.

- If $-2 \times 3 = -6$, what if you started with $-6 \div 3$?

- How could you use the multiplication problem to give you the answer?

Help students see that the general rules—same signs yield a positive result, different signs yield a negative result—are true for both multiplication and division.

4 Creating Statements and Counterexamples

In small groups, have students create a set of statements about signed number operations. Some should be always true and some should not always be true. This will encourage students to use what they have learned about signed number operations and counterexamples. If students need more guidance, suggest that they look at Hyun and Tanya's list of statements and their solutions from Lesson 1, and create some of their own like those. Make sure students save their statements to use in Lesson 4.

5 Discussing the Statements

After students have finished their sets of statements, bring the class together for a discussion on mathematical statements involving four operations and counterexamples. You could use questions such as those below for this discussion. Remind students to be prepared to justify their statements.

- Do you think this statement is always true? Why or why not?

- Did you think of any counterexamples? If so, explain them.

- If the statement is not always true, how could you restate it so that it *is* always true?

what to look for

Investigate Division of Signed Numbers

Now that you have used cubes to model multiplying different combinations of signed numbers, the next step is to think about division. You may use cubes and what you know about the relationship between multiplication and division as you work on these division problems.

$$-6 \div (-3) = ?$$

How can you use what you know about multiplication to think about division of signed numbers?

1 List all the different combinations of two signed numbers that could be used in a division problem.

2 For each combination you listed, write some sample problems. Think about what you know about the relationship between multiplication and division before you write down the answers to your sample division problems.

3 Write down any conclusions you can make about the results when dividing each combination.

Create Statements and Counterexamples

In your group, make up eight statements about operations with positive and negative numbers. Four of your statements should always be true. Four of your statements should not always be true and should have counterexamples. Try to include some statements that are true in some cases and others that are always false. Make sure you include all four operations in the eight statements: addition, subtraction, multiplication, and division.

On a separate sheet of paper, make an answer key for your statements that shows:

- the statement

- whether it is always true or not always true

- one counterexample, if the statement is not always true

hot **words** | signed numbers counterexample

HW**omework**
page 36

4

Summarizing Rules for Operating with Integers

Rules to Operate By

Students who had little experience with problems requiring more independent thinking found it difficult to come up with addition and subtraction problems that have the same answer. I provided a model for them: 3 + (−3) = and they had to find the answer. One student then popped up with 5 + (−5) = and his classmates answered. They were not comfortable branching out on their own. When they got to the multiplication and division problems their success was evident. I had the students initially use the same four numbers (3, −3, 5, −5) and added the other two numbers (15, −15) after a few minutes. I felt this was essential to allow them to reacquaint themselves with the more complicated multiplication/division problems. □

student page

1 Finding Operations that Are Equivalent

After students have had a chance to work on item **1** on Student Guide page 12, stop the class to discuss the results from addition and subtraction before going on to investigate equivalent statements for multiplication and division. First summarize the two different sets of four problems that students come up with that have the same answer (problems that equal 2 and problems that equal −2 shown in the note) using these questions:

- What are two problems that give the same answer? Can you find other examples?

- What general rule can you state about operations that give you the same result?

- Will this always be true? Can you find any counterexamples?

- What other combinations of addition or subtraction with signed numbers are equivalent to another combination?

Then summarize the situations in which the operations of addition and subtraction are equivalent: Adding a positive is equivalent to subtracting a negative, and adding a negative is equivalent to subtracting a positive. You may want to ask students whether they can find similar situations

in which multiplication and division are equivalent. Then have students complete item **2** in the Student Guide and come up with a general rule for the result when multiplying and dividing with integers.

There are two different sets of four problems involving addition or subtraction that students can come up with using the numbers 3, −3, 5, and −5. (Problems that equal 2: $5 - 3 = 2$, $-3 - (-5) = 2$, $5 + (-3) = 2$, $-3 + 5 = 2$. Problems that equal −2: $-5 + 3 = -2$, $3 + (-5) = -2$, $-5 - (-3) = -2$, $3 - 5 = -2$.) Answers for the multiplication and division equations will vary, but some possibilities are: $3 \times 5 = 15$; $-3 \times 5 = -15$; $3 \times (-5) = -15$; $5 \times 5 = 25$; $5 \times 5 \times (-3) = -75$; $15 \div (-3) = -5$; $-15 \div (-5) = 3$; $-15 \div (-3) = 5$; $-15 \div 5 \div (-3) = 1$; $15 \div (-15) \div (-3) = \frac{1}{3}$.

2 Discussing a General Rule for Multiplying or Dividing

When students have completed item **2** on Student Guide page 12, ask them to share the equations they came up with and discuss any conclusions they were able to make. Summarize these general rules for multiplication and division:

- When the signs are the same, the product or quotient is positive.

- When the signs are different, the product or quotient is negative.

homework options

LESSON HOMEWORK

Making Mathematical Arguments
Student Guide page 37
Solutions: Assessment page A32

hot **topics**

• *Integer Operations*
• *Statistics*

---

negative
1. -5+3=-2
-5-3=-2
-5+3=-2
3-5=-2

positive
5+-3=2
5-3=2
-3+5=2
-3--5=2

• Adding a negative is like subtr...
• Adding a positive is negative.
3 × -3 = -9

=8 5+3=8
=8 5--3=8

• The statement saying that two signs of the same kind equals a positive 25 is true. There are no counter examples, adding a positive is like subtracting a negative.

×5=-15   -3×5=-15
×-3=-15 -5×3=-15
5÷3=   -15÷5=-3
         -15÷-3=-5
5÷5=3   -3×15=-45
         -5×15=-75
75÷5=-3 -5×-5=3
-15÷-3= -15÷-5=3
-3×-5=15 5×3=15

• If the problem has two of the same signs when multiplied or divided together the answer will be positive.

• If the problem has two different signs when being multiplied or divided together the answer will be negative.

---

4 Rules to Operate By

SUMMARIZING
RULES FOR
OPERATING WITH
INTEGERS

In this lesson, you will think about rules for adding, subtracting, multiplying, and dividing with signed numbers. As you think about what operations might be equivalent and about counterexamples, you will be summarizing what you have learned about signed number operations in this phase.

Find Operations that Are Equivalent

Which operations with signed numbers are equivalent?

1 Using 3, −3, 5, and −5, write as many different addition and subtraction problems as you can that have the answer 2 or –2.

  a. Look at the problems you wrote and think about when adding and subtracting are equivalent, or when you get the same result.

  b. Write statements about when you think adding and subtracting are equivalent. Will the statements you have written always be true? Can you find any counterexamples?

2 Write down all the multiplication and division equations you can using combinations of the numbers 3, −3, 5, −5, 15, and −15. Use the equations you write to help you think about these questions:

  a. Can you write a general rule for multiplication and division problems that have positive answers?

  b. Can you write a general rule for multiplication and division problems that have negative answers?

Few students had problems with determining whether or not the answer would be positive or negative when multiplying several numbers together. Many shared their findings with their tablemates. I did notice that some students could master the appropriate "signs" but began making computational errors. I figured this was due to the concentration placed on the signs and not the math. One student provided an example of a common oversight when giving a counterexample: $-3 \times 3 = -6$. So I would typically respond with, "Sure, the answer should be negative, but is 3 times 3 actually 6?" □

Before students wrote and tested their statements about multiplication and division, I suggested that they include examples that mix multiplication and division with addition and subtraction. This resulted in some mathematically-interesting statements. □

student page

3 Determining Whether a Statement Is Always True

In this step, students should apply what they know about counterexamples and addition and subtraction of integers. You may want to add to or replace statements on the list with statements written by students in Lesson 3.

Of the seven statements listed in the Student Guide, students should find that counterexamples exist for Positive + Negative = Negative, Positive − Positive = Positive, and Negative − Negative = Negative.

student page

4 Writing and Testing Statements About Multiplication and Division

Before students begin this investigation, you may want to remind them of the general rules they wrote for multiplication and division problems that involve two numbers. The purpose of this step is to get students to think about situations in which there are more than two factors or that mix multiplication and division. It is also an opportunity to determine whether students are able to come up with statements and test them with counterexamples. Encourage students to show all their work. Let students know that you are interested in seeing statements they made and disproved with counterexamples, not just statements they were able to make that are always true.

The solutions to the first four problems are as follows: If one or three negative numbers are multiplied, the answer is negative; if two or four negative numbers are multiplied, the answer is positive. A students might write: "If the number of negative numbers is even, the answer will be positive. If the number of negative numbers is odd, the answer will be negative." A counterexample might include zero among the numbers multiplied, so the answer will be zero regardless of the number of negative numbers. Students could modify the rule to say: "When several nonzero numbers are multiplied together, the answer will be positive if the number of negative numbers is even and negative if the number of negative numbers is odd." To include division, students might write: "When several nonzero numbers are multiplied or divided together, the answer will be positive if the number of negative numbers is even and negative if the number of negative numbers is odd."

- *equivalencies—that subtracting a negative is equivalent to adding a positive, and that subtracting a positive is equivalent to adding a negative?*
- *how to find counterexamples?*
- *the rule for multiplying and dividing several signed numbers together?*

See *Making Mathematical Arguments* Assessment page A9 for assessment information.

• Positive + Positive = Positive "Always true" because you aren't adding any negatives or subtr[...]

• Positive + Negative = Negative 2 + 3 = 5

• Negative + Negative = Negative "Always true" because you aren't adding any positives or subtracting any negatives.

• Positive - Positive = Positive 5 - 6 = -1

• Positive - Negative = Positive "Always true" because you are taking the negative away from the positive just leaving more positive.

• Negative - Positive = Negative "always true" because you are taking the positive away from the negative leaving more negative.

Negative - Negative = Negative -3 - -4 = +1

negative, with 1 neg. #
positive, with 2 neg #s
c. negative, with 3 neg #s
d. positive, with 4 neg. #'s

a long multiplication problem with many negatives it might positive or negative. If there are an even amount of neg.s the answer will be positive. If there are a odd amount re are no counterexamples.

tiplication and division have the same answer so our statement will always be true.

Determine Whether a Statement Is Always True

Look at the statements in the box below.

- If you can find a counterexample, write the statement and its counterexample.

- If you cannot find a counterexample and believe that a statement is always true, write the statement "Always True." Then explain why you think it is always true.

How can you apply what you know about integer addition and subtraction and counterexamples?

Is It Always True?
Positive + Positive = Positive
Positive + Negative = Negative
Negative + Negative = Negative
Positive − Positive = Positive
Positive − Negative = Positive
Negative − Positive = Negative
Negative − Negative = Negative

Write and Test Statements About Multiplication and Division

1 For each problem below, tell whether the answer will be positive or negative and how many negative numbers are multiplied.

a. $2 \times (-2)$

b. $2 \times (-2) \times (-2)$

c. $2 \times (-2) \times (-2) \times (-2)$

d. $2 \times (-2) \times (-2) \times (-2) \times (-2)$

2 Write a statement that tells whether your answer will be positive or negative when you multiply several numbers together.

3 Can you find a counterexample to the statement you wrote about multiplication? If so, rewrite your statement so that it is always true.

4 Using what you have learned about multiplication, write a statement that tells whether your answer will be positive or negative when the problem uses division.

hot **words** | signed numbers counterexample

page 37

MAKING MATHEMATICAL ARGUMENTS LESSON 4
© Creative Publications • MathScape **13**

A TEACHER REFLECTS

Investigating Signed Numbers

At the beginning of this phase, I paired students up and each was provided with a set of 20 centimeter cubes, 10 green and 10 pink. We immediately designated the green cubes as negative. Students had minimal integer background before starting this unit, and some knew that a $(-)$ in front of a number signified "negative" and not "subtract."

Most students preferred to make a number line on the top of their papers that went from (-10) to $(+10)$ which helped them with Lesson 1. As we progressed through this lesson, many students questioned certain vocabulary words that they were not familiar with and I wrote the words and the explanation on the board. Some of the words were: negative, positive, sum, and product. I also added the symbol beside the word and kept this on the board for students to reference.

As students began modeling the problems using the color cubes, their confidence soared. Many of the quieter girls were willing to present their potential solutions on the overhead to their peers… and they were correct. They beamed!

When I asked them to demonstrate another way to obtain an answer of $(+5)$, Grace immediately offered $8 + (-3)$. She had noticed a pattern that enabled her to find the answer. I asked her another question to see if she understood the concept and could see past the "pattern." She instantly figured out that $15 + (-1)$ would be 14.

My ESL students began to get lost with the term "signed" numbers. I tried using this term to refer to "positives" and "negatives," but they couldn't get past the "plus/minus" terms. I often heard them asking one another, "How do you plus a minus?" Referring to a number line and having them move a cube on top of it was quite effective for these students. It also aided those students who clearly understood the concepts as they explained them to their tablemates. I was ecstatic to see the amount of responsibility the students took upon themselves to insure that their tablemates were successful! This was a "warm fuzzy" lesson for me.

Roots, Rules, and Arguments

While examining mathematical arguments about squares, cubes, roots, and exponents, students explore special cases to write arguments that are always true.

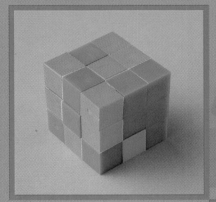

LESSON 5

Perfect Pattern Predictions

Students look for a rule to describe a pattern in square numbers, or *perfect squares*. Using physical cubes and tables to explore the increases between any two perfect squares, students find a method to predict this increase. Students use their method to write a rule and then expand the rule to include negative square roots. This forms the basis for learning about mathematical arguments in the next lesson.

Mathematical Goals

- Gain familiarity with perfect squares and square roots.

- Find linear patterns and make generalized statements that describe the patterns.

- Relate a mathematical process to a visual model.

- Use inverse operations to solve problems.

MATERIALS

PER STUDENT

- calculator

PER PAIR

- several handfuls of Rainbow Centimeter Cubes

PREPARATION

Make sure you know how to use the $\sqrt{x}$ key on a calculator. Review the information about calculators on page 35.

LESSON 6

Counterexamples and Special Cases

In this lesson, students learn about the role of special cases in formulating mathematical arguments. They begin by looking at a mathematical argument written by a fictitious student. Then they examine the special cases, 0, 1, negative integers, and fractions, before focusing on fractions. At the end of the lesson, students revise the mathematical argument to make it always true.

Mathematical Goals

- Learn to check for special cases when making a mathematical argument.

- Look for a counterexample as the first step in making a mathematical argument.

- Develop better understanding of multiplication of fractions.

- Relate a visual model to a mathematical process.

MATERIALS

PER STUDENT

- calculator

- Rainbow Centimeter Cubes, fraction circles, and other manipulatives that pertain to fractions, such as fraction bars.

- Reproducible R11

PREPARATION

You can use Guidelines for Writing Your Own Mathematical Argument, R12, reproducible as a transparency or distribute copies to students for use in subsequent lessons. It is also on Student Guide, page 19.

LESSON 7

Root Relationships

In this lesson, students examine a mathematical argument about cube numbers and cube roots. As students look at positive and negative square and cube roots, they devise their own rules which summarize their understanding of the relationship of squares to square roots, and cubes to cube roots. At the end of this lesson, students write their own mathematical arguments.

MATERIALS

PER STUDENT

- calculator

PER GROUP OF FOUR

- 40 Rainbow Centimeter Cubes

Mathematical Goals

- Relate cubes and cube roots to a visual model.
- Find perfect cubes and both positive and negative cube roots.
- Devise rules about positive and negative cube roots and square roots.
- Write a complete mathematical argument.

LESSON 8

A Powerful Argument

This lesson serves as an assessment for the phase. Students explore a chart of powers of different numbers and search for perfect squares in the chart. The patterns formed by the location of the perfect squares helps students understand more about squares, roots, and exponents. Each student chooses one of the patterns as the basis for writing his or her own mathematical argument.

MATERIALS

PER STUDENT

- calculator

PER GROUP OF FOUR

- 40 Rainbow Centimeter Cubes

Mathematical Goals

- Find powers of a number.
- Gain a better understanding of squares, roots, and exponents.
- Write a complete mathematical argument about a perfect square pattern.

MATH BACKGROUND

Finding Patterns in the Powers Chart

In Lesson 8, students create a chart of powers of different numbers and search for the perfect squares in the chart. The location of the perfect squares results in an interesting pattern. The patterns and the mathematical reason for the patterns are explained below.

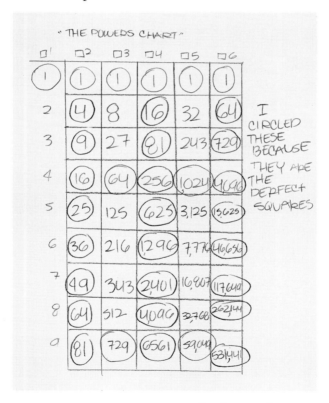

Perfect squares appear in the n^2, n^4, and n^6 columns, as well as in the 1, 4, and 9 rows.

The Case of n^4 and n^6

Each number in the n^4 column is created by multiplying some number by itself four times. Pairs of factors can be multiplied together to create two new factors whose product is in the column. Because there are an even number of factors, they can always be grouped into a pair of products, and therefore form a perfect square.

$$\underbrace{3 \times 3}_{9} \times \underbrace{3 \times 3}_{9} = 81$$
$$9 \times 9 = 81$$

The same is true for numbers in the n^6 column. The six factors can be regrouped into a pair of products, and thus form perfect squares.

$$\underbrace{3 \times 3 \times 3}_{27} \times \underbrace{3 \times 3 \times 3}_{27} = 729$$
$$27 \times 27 = 729$$

The 1, 4, and 9 rows are similar. The 1 row will have all 1's in it, so, trivially, they are all perfect squares.

The 4 row consists of powers of 4. Because 4 is a perfect square, each 4 can be expressed as 2×2. The first 2 in each pair can be attributed to the first factor, and the second 2 can be attributed to the second factor. So no matter what power 4 is raised to, the result will always be a perfect square. The same is true for 9. Because 9 is a perfect square (3×3), each 3 can be attributed to one of the two roots of the perfect square.

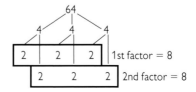

TECHNOLOGY OPTIONS

Use of a calculator, either a standard four function calculator or a scientific calculator, such as the TI Explorer Plus, is fundamental to the investigations in Phases Two and Three of the unit. You may want to review with students the following procedures for squaring and cubing numbers and for finding the square root on most calculators.

To square a number:

Enter the number you want to square. Press $\boxed{\times}$ and $\boxed{=}$. For example, to square 23 enter $\boxed{2}\boxed{3}\boxed{\times}$ $\boxed{=}$ to get the answer (529).

To find the square root of a number:

Enter the number for which you want to find the square root, then press $\boxed{\sqrt{}}$. For example, to find the square root of 81, enter $\boxed{8}\boxed{1}\boxed{\sqrt{}}$ to get the answer (9).

To cube a number:

Enter the number you want to cube. Press $\boxed{\times}$ and $\boxed{=}\boxed{=}$. For example, to cube 14 enter $\boxed{1}\boxed{4}\boxed{\times}\boxed{=}$ $\boxed{=}$ to get the answer 2,744.

To cube a fraction:

Convert the fraction you want to cube to a decimal by dividing. For example, to convert $\frac{1}{4}$ enter $\boxed{1}\boxed{\div}\boxed{4}\boxed{=}$. Press $\boxed{\times}$ and $\boxed{=}\boxed{=}$ to get the answer (0.015625). This is the same as $\frac{1}{64}$ which can be checked by $\boxed{1}\boxed{\div}\boxed{6}\boxed{4}\boxed{=}$ on the calculator.

If students have access to a scientific calculator, such as the TI Explorer Plus, they will be able to use the $\boxed{x^y}$ or $\boxed{y^x}$ key to find cube roots. However, all of the investigations in the unit have been structured so that they may be done without a scientific calculator.

If students have calculators that do not have cube root keys, introduce them to the method of successive approximations to find the cube root of a number. With this method, students narrow down the possibilities by using the calculator to cube numbers. For instance, $\sqrt[3]{17}$ is between 2 and 3 because it is between $\sqrt[3]{8}$ and $\sqrt[3]{27}$. Show students that they can estimate the cube root to be about 2.5 and check this by using the calculator to cube 2.5. Since the result is 15.625, students can conclude that $\sqrt[3]{17}$ must be greater than 2.5 and try cubing 2.6, which results in 17.576. Now they can see that $\sqrt[3]{17}$ lies somewhere between 2.5 and 2.6, but is a little closer to 2.6, and will try cubing numbers such as 2.57 (16.974593) and 2.58 (17.173512). Therefore, $\sqrt[3]{17}$ must be between 2.57 and 2.58. It's up to you and the students how long to continue the process.

Students enjoyed making the table of perfect squares and discovering the patterns. Before noticing the pattern, several students were counting on their fingers under the table to check the increase between 36 and 49, for example. Calculators were imperative so students could concentrate on the patterns without being bogged down with the computational aspects. Some students did not put any number in the "Increased by" column because it had not increased. This made all of their columns off by one line. For my next class, I suggested that they draw horizontal lines for each row in the table or use lined paper. □

Perfect Pattern Predictions

Have students review the phase overview on pages 14–15 in the Student Guide.

1 Discussing a Perfect Square

Give each pair of students several handfuls of small cubes, and have them make squares of different sizes out of the cubes. Have them arrange the squares in increasing order as shown on Student Guide page 16. By answering questions such as those below, students will better understand the meaning of perfect squares.

- What sequence of numbers does this generate?

- Why are these numbers called "perfect squares"? What other numbers are perfect squares?

- How would you write these numbers using exponents? (Establish that 6^2 can be named "6 to the second power" or "6 squared." The latter is more common.)

- Why do people say "6 squared" for 6^2?

Discuss the term "square root" with students, so that they can differentiate between the term "square" and "square root." Encourage students to use these terms when discussing their ideas throughout this lesson. You might also want to demonstrate to students how to use a calculator to find a square and square root as shown on page 35.

student page

2 Investigating Perfect Squares

Students should see that each perfect square increases by the next consecutive odd number; i.e., the pattern of increase is 3, 5, 7, 9, 11, ... Once students understand this, they will feel more confident about solving problems that require extending the table.

The increase of 21 lies between the perfect squares 100 and 121. The increase of 27 lies between the perfect squares 169 and 196. The increase of 35 lies between the perfect squares 289 and 324.

LESSON HOMEWORK

Making Mathematical Arguments
Student Guide page 38
Solutions: Assessment page A33

hot **topics**

• *Powers and Exponents*
• *Square and Cube Roots*

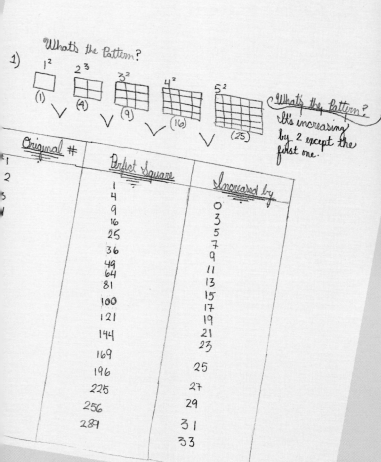

1) "What's the Pattern?"

1^2 2^3 3^2 4^2 5^2

(1)   (4)   (9)   (16)   (25)

"What's the Pattern?"
It's increasing
by 2 except the
first one.

Original #	Perfect Square	Increased by
1	1	
2	4	0
3	9	3
	16	5
	25	7
	36	9
	49	11
	64	13
	81	15
	100	17
	121	19
	144	21
	169	23
	196	25
	225	27
	256	29
	289	31
		33

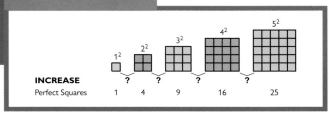

5 Perfect Pattern Predictions

EXPLORING
PATTERNS IN
PERFECT SQUARES

Any number multiplied by itself is called the square of that number. When the number that is multiplied by itself is an integer, the result is called a perfect square. In the last phase, you found rules for signed number operations. Can you find a rule to describe a pattern in perfect squares?

Investigate Perfect Squares

What is the pattern in the increase from one perfect square to another?

Look at the perfect squares shown in the box What's the Pattern? The number that is multiplied by itself to produce each square is called the square root. For example, the square root of 9 is 3. We can use a radical sign to write this as $\sqrt{9} = 3$.

1 The box What's the Pattern? shows the perfect squares that result when you square each whole number from 1 through 5. By how much is each perfect square increasing sequentially?

2 Make a table showing the increase when each whole number from 1 through 12 is squared. Label your table with three columns: Original Number, Perfect Square, and Increased By.

3 Extend your table to find between which two perfect squares the increase will be 21, 27, and 35.

What's the Pattern?

| | 1^2 | 2^2 | 3^2 | 4^2 | 5^2 |

INCREASE

| Perfect Squares | 1 | 4 | 9 | 16 | 25 |
| | ? | ? | ? | ? | |

One way a student came up with to show how each new square can be formed was to add two lengths equal to the length of one side on the previous square, plus one more cube for the bottom right corner. □

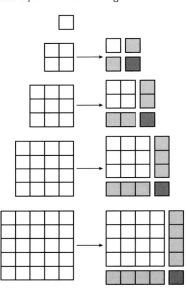

student page

3 Finding a Method to Predict the Increase

The steps in this investigation move students from concrete examples and reliance on extending their tables to general statements. Make sure students have cubes available to experiment with. It is important that students focus on the relationship between the manipulatives and the pattern. If students can describe how the pattern they see relates to the physical model, they may find it easier to predict increases following perfect square numbers that are too large to figure out simply by extending the table.

Even though students are working with cubes to model perfect squares, when they draw diagrams of their cubes, they should be encouraged to draw two-dimensional grid representations, like those shown on Student Guide page 16.

4 Discussing the Method

After students have completed their investigations to find methods, use questions such as those below to discuss their different methods and to reach some agreement about what the pattern for the increase is.

- What is the pattern you used in your method?

- How did you figure out your method?

- How does each step in your method relate to the cubes?

The ways students identify the pattern for the increase will vary. In general, the increase from one perfect square to the next has the form $2n + 1$, where n is equal to the square root of the smaller perfect square. For example, the increase after 10^2 will be $2(10) + 1$. This can be represented by the equation: $(n + 1)^2 - n^2 = 2n + 1$. Some students may use variables, while others may just describe this relationship in words. Whatever methods they use, students should find that the increase after the perfect square 529 is 47. The increase after the perfect square 1,089 is 67. The increase after the perfect square 2,401 is 99.

student page

5 Writing a Rule for the Pattern

Encourage students to try to write their rule in one sentence, keeping it as succinct as possible. Some students may have written their rules when they found their methods and may only need to revise a little.

You may want to spend some time explaining positive and negative square roots. Make sure students understand what the positive and negative square roots of a positive number are and how to write them. For example, 5 is the positive square root of 25 and -5 is the negative square root of 25. In testing the rule with negative square roots, students will find that the pattern does not hold true and will need to revise the rule, $2n + 1$, to make it clear that n is a whole number greater than 0.

Find a Method to Predict the Increase

Come up with a method for figuring out the increase between any two perfect squares. You may find it helpful to use a calculator to investigate squares and square roots in coming up with a method.

1 Use words, diagrams, or equations to explain your method.

2 Think about how each step in your method relates to the way the perfect squares are shown with cubes. What do the numbers in your method represent in the cubes?

3 Use your method to figure out the increase between each of the following perfect squares and the perfect square that comes next: 529; 1,089; 2,401.

> **How can you predict the increase between any two perfect squares?**

Write a Rule for the Pattern

Think about the method you came up with for predicting the increase for any perfect square.

* Write a rule that describes how to predict what the increase between perfect squares will be.

* Every positive square number has a positive and a negative square root. For example, 36 has square roots of 6 and -6 since $6^2 = 36$ and $(-6)^2 = 36$. -6 is the negative square root of 36. Does the rule you wrote work for the negative square root? If so, give examples. If not, give counterexamples and revise your rule.

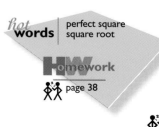

hot **words** | perfect square
square root

Homework

 page 38

MAKING MATHEMATICAL ARGUMENTS   LESSON 5
© Creative Publications • MathScape   **17**

Formulating a Mathematical Argument

I wanted students to think more about what special cases exist. We discussed the difference between natural numbers, whole numbers, integers, and rational numbers. □

When we got to Dan's argument and were talking about fractions, I realized that my students might be more familiar with multiplying decimals than fractions. (In class, we frequently converted fractions to decimals before multiplying.) When I asked if Dan's argument was true for fractions, one student said, "It's not true for a half," and wrote "0.5 × 0.5 = 0.25" on the board. I asked if it was true when a half was written "$\frac{1}{2}$" and how we could show it. This helped the class review fractions. □

Counterexamples and Special Cases

1 Examining a Mathematical Argument

Ask students to read over Dan's Mathematical Argument or read it together as a class. This shows a mathematical argument made by a fictitious student. Students will explore the validity of this argument throughout this lesson.

> 👆 As students have already learned in the first phase, a rule is really a statement that has been shown to be always true. Dan neglected to test his rule for all kinds of numbers. Students will think about this in the class discussion in Step 3.

2 Finding Counterexamples to Dan's Rule

Before students work in small groups to find counterexamples to Dan's rule, you may want to brainstorm examples of special cases with the class. Some examples are positive integers, negative integers, fractions, and zero.

> 👆 Some students may be a little unsure about how to raise a fraction to a power. You might need to help them see that it simply means multiplying fractions, which should be familiar to them.

3 Discussing Dan's Rule

Divide the class into small groups. After students have spent some time in their group investigation, bring the class together for a discussion about whether or not Dan has written a good mathematical argument. As part of this discussion, address the four special cases that will be used in this phase: 0, 1, negative integers, and fractions.

- What do you think of Dan's argument?

- Can you find any counterexamples to Dan's rule?

- What is the smallest number for which Dan's rule is true? What is the largest number?

- What happens to Dan's rule if you use 0? 1? negative numbers? fractions?

- Did Dan's rule statement turn out to always be true?

Explain to students that they will be paying special attention to fractions and looking at why the square of a fraction is smaller than the original fraction.

LESSON HOMEWORK

Making Mathematical Arguments
Student Guide page 39
Solutions: Assessment page A34

hot topics

- *Powers and Exponents*
- *Counterexamples*

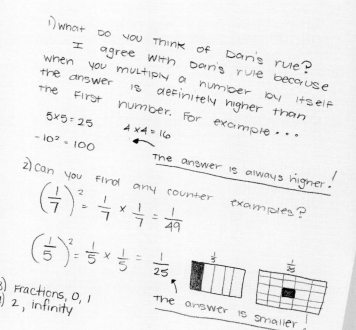

1) What do you think of Dan's rule?
I agree with Dan's rule because
when you multiply a number by itself
the answer is definitely higher than
the first number. For example...

$5 \times 5 = 25$ $4 \times 4 = 16$

$-10^2 = 100$

The answer is always higher!

2) Can you find any counter examples?

$\left(\frac{1}{7}\right)^2 = \frac{1}{7} \times \frac{1}{7} = \frac{1}{49}$

$\left(\frac{1}{5}\right)^2 = \frac{1}{5} \times \frac{1}{5} = \frac{1}{25}$

The answer is smaller!

3) Fractions, 0, 1
4) 2, infinity

---

6 Counterexamples and Special Cases

FORMULATING A
MATHEMATICAL
ARGUMENT

In Lesson 5, you investigated patterns in perfect squares when positive and negative integers are squared. In this lesson, you will examine a mathematical argument about the result of squaring any number, looking for counterexamples and checking for special cases of numbers. This will help you think of ways to revise the mathematical argument so that it is always true.

Find Counterexamples to Dan's Rule

How can you examine a mathematical argument to find counterexamples?

After you have read Dan's Mathematical Argument, work with your group to try to find counterexamples to Dan's rule. Work through some or all of these questions:

1 What do you think of Dan's rule?

2 Can you find any specific counterexamples for Dan's rule?

3 Can you find any special cases for which the whole case is a counterexample?

4 What do you think is the smallest number for which Dan's rule is true? the largest number?

Dan's Mathematical Argument

What is my rule? My rule states: "The square of any number is always larger than the original number." For example, if I start with the number 8 and square it, I get 64. 64 is definitely larger than 8.

How did I figure out my rule? I started by choosing different numbers, like 3, 8, 12, 47 and 146. Each time I squared them, I got a larger number. I saw that as the original numbers got larger, the square numbers also got larger very quickly.

For what special cases is my rule true? I tried small and large numbers, like 3 and 146, and my rule was always true.

Original Number	Square Number
3	9
8	64
12	144
47	2,209
146	21,316

Some of my students got frustrated with making sketches because they could not make some of the fractions that they wanted to explore. So the next day, I gave these students a protractor and a handout with a blank circle. We did a mini-lesson on how to divide the circle into fractional parts, after which these students created some fraction circle pieces of their own. □

4 Finding Out About Squares of Fractions

Distribute a copy of Investigating Squares of Fractions, Reproducible R11, to each student. After students have read over the reproducible, ask them to explore ways to model an explanation for this question using manipulatives or sketches. Make sure you have manipulatives available for students' use.

This investigation is intended to serve several purposes. It helps students develop a better understanding of how the operation of multiplication works and how it applies to fractions. It gives students an opportunity to create visual models that help them develop their own understanding. During this investigation, students may also come to understand why Dan's rule would not apply to fractions.

5 Sharing the Different Methods

Ask different students to take turns showing their methods for investigating squares of fractions to the class. As students demonstrate their methods, help the class think about the questions below. You may want students to revise their explanations after the class discussion.

- Is this method like your own method? Are the two methods equivalent?

- Does this method give you any ideas for how to improve your explanation?

6 Revising a Mathematical Argument

Let students know that Dan's mathematical argument is not quite right and that it is missing some important information. Encourage students to use the guidelines shown in the Student Guide as they write their own revisions to the mathematical argument. Students will use these guidelines throughout the unit to write mathematical arguments.

You may want to use this opportunity to introduce absolute value. The absolute value of a number is its distance from zero on the number line, or, equivalently, the number's value without its plus or minus sign. Students may revise the rule as follows: The square of any number greater than 1 is always larger than the original number. The square of any number less than -1 is always larger than the absolute value of the original number. The square of 0 is 0 and the square of 1 is 1.

what to look for

DO STUDENTS' MATHEMATICAL ARGUMENTS:

- *show an understanding of square numbers?*
- *state the rule clearly and in a general way so that it can apply to more than just a few numbers?*
- *describe methods used to figure out the rule and include counterexamples for which the rule did not work?*
- *include an explanation of special cases for which the rule does not work?*

See *Making Mathematical Arguments* Assessment page A9 for assessment information.

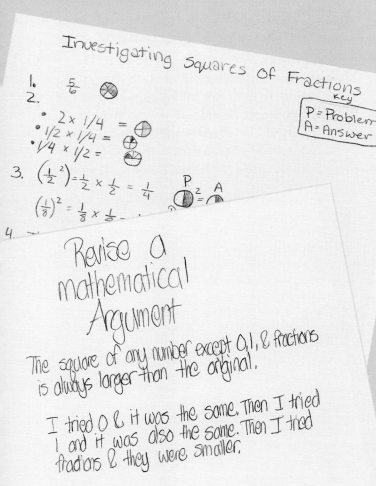

Revise a Mathematical Argument

Think about Dan's Mathematical Argument and read it again if necessary. Write a new version of the argument that is correct and complete. Use the different points below as guidelines to make sure you have included all the information necessary to make your argument a strong one. Show all of your work.

1 What is your rule?

  a. Did you state your rule clearly?

  b. Could someone who had not already done the problem understand your rule?

  c. Did you describe your rule generally so that it can apply to more than just a few numbers?

2 How did you figure out your rule?

  a. What methods did you use to figure out your rule?

  b. What counterexamples did you find where your rule did not work?

3 Does your rule apply to special cases?

  a. Does your rule work for 0? for 1? for fractions? for negative numbers?

  b. Are there other cases for which your rule works or does not work?

  c. If your rule does not work for some cases, explain why it doesn't.

How can you make a mathematical argument that is always true?

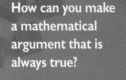

hot **words** | square number
absolute value

Ho**mework**
👫 page 39

MAKING MATHEMATICAL ARGUMENTS LESSON 6
© Creative Publications • MathScape   **19**

**Writing and Revising
a Mathematical
Argument**

*In one class, my
students focused on
the dimensions of
the cubes that they
constructed from the manipulatives, and not on the total number
of pieces that made up the cube.
So in my second class, I posed the
question, "What is the smallest
number of pieces that would make
a cube?" This focused my students
on the total number of pieces.
When my students described the
dimensions of their cubes, I fol-
lowed up with the question, "And
how many pieces were in the
cube?" On the board, I wrote
3 × 3 × 3 = 27.* □

Root
Relationships

1 Exploring Perfect Cubes

Before students open the Student Guide, show
the class a cube or draw a cube on the board. Ask
students to describe the characteristics of the
cube. Make sure students understand that a cube
has length, width, and height, and that all three
dimensions are of equal measure. Explain to students that they will be looking at *cubic numbers*
in this lesson, but do not give the definition of a
cubic number yet.

Arrange students in groups of four and distribute
40 cubes to each group to use as they explore the
questions below. To build a cube of 64, two
groups of four will need to share their cubes.
During this exploration, students will begin to
generate lists of perfect cubes and will think
about the relationship of the manipulatives to
perfect cubes and cube roots.

- What numbers of cubes can you arrange into a
  larger cube? Find all the different arrangements
  that you can with the cubes that you have and
  make a list of the numbers.

- Why do you think these numbers are called
  cubic numbers or *perfect cubes*?

- What are some other perfect cubes? How did
  you find them?

- You have already learned what a square root is.
  What do you think a cube root is?

- How would you use the little cubes to show
  what a cube root is?

student page

2 Verifying Dan's Mathematical Argument

After students have read through Dan's 2nd
Mathematical Argument, ask them to check if
Dan's argument is always true. Although Dan
tested for decimals, he did not test thoroughly
because he neglected to test for decimals less than 1.
This argument, like Dan's first mathematical argument from the previous lesson, is not always true.

In order to do this investigation, students need to
know how to find a cube number and cube
root. Encourage students to start with the cube
root and multiply that number three times to get the cube
number. Students will need to use estimation to figure out
the cube root of a decimal. You might want to demonstrate to students a way to use a calculator to find the
cube number for a fraction. See page 35 for more information. Students should find that Dan's rule is not true for
0, 1, fractions, and negative numbers.

LESSON HOMEWORK

Making Mathematical Arguments
Student Guide page 40
Solutions: Assessment page A35

hot **topics**

- *Powers and Exponents*
- *Square and Cube Roots*

Verify Dan's Mathematical
Argument

1. $0^3 = 0$
   $1^3 = 1$
   $\frac{1}{4}^3 = \frac{1}{64}$
   $-2^3 = -8$

2. It's not true for 0 (It's the same)
   It's not true for 1 (It's the same)
   It's not true for fractions (It's less)
   It's not true for negatives (It's less)

3. no

---

7 Root Relationships

WRITING AND
REVISING A
MATHEMATICAL
ARGUMENT

You have already learned what a square root is and investigated mathematical arguments involving square numbers and square roots. In this lesson, you will explore cubic numbers and cube roots. A cubic number is a number that results when you multiply the same number times itself three times.

Verify Dan's Mathematical Argument

What is missing from Dan's mathematical argument?

Follow the steps below to verify if Dan's argument is always true.

1 Check Dan's argument for counterexamples. List them and show why they do not fit Dan's rule.

2 Check Dan's argument for special cases. Is his rule true for 0, 1, fractions, and negative numbers? For each case, show the original number (or numbers) and describe how it compares to the cube number.

3 Do you have any special cases of your own that you want to check? Try them out and describe what you find.

Dan's 2nd Mathematical Argument

What is my rule? My rule states: "The cube of any number is always larger than the original number." For example, if I start with the number 3 and cube it, I get 27 and 27 is definitely larger than 3.

How did I figure out my rule? I started by choosing different numbers, like 2, 2.2, 3, 3.5, and 4. Each time I cubed them, I got a larger number. I saw that as the original numbers got larger, the cube numbers also got larger.

For what special cases is my rule true? I tried whole numbers and decimals, like 2 and 2.2, and my rule was always true.

Original Number	Square Number
2	8
2.2	10.648
3	27
3.5	42.875
4	64

MAKING MATHEMATICAL ARGUMENTS LESSON 7
20 © Creative Publications • MathScape

Most students just reiterated the rule they originally learned about squares and cubes. They know that a negative times a negative would be positive and were able to carry that over to "squaring" a negative number. They stumbled a little more on the cube roots, so I had them draw and build the problems and potential answers with the different colored cubes. This helped! □

When students had to evaluate other student's arguments, some were apprehensive so I put the writing prompts on an overhead for them to copy. I felt that for some students a blank sheet of paper on which to write comments was intimidating. The prompts on the overhead seemed to give these students more confidence in evaluating their peers. □

student page

3 Looking at Square and Cube Roots

For this investigation you can point out to students that any number can be cubed. If the original number is an integer, then cubing it results in a perfect cube. Likewise, one can find the cube root of any number. If the original number is a perfect cube, then students might recognize what its cube root value is. After students have checked for special cases, they can expand their thinking into exploring positive and negative cube roots and square roots. Make sure students understand that they will be sharing and discussing the rules that they find in this investigation with the class.

👆 You cannot find a positive square root or cube root for a negative number. You cannot find a negative square root for a negative number and you cannot find a negative cube root for a positive number. Students may come up with the following rules: "The cube root of a negative number is always negative;" "The cube root of a positive number is always positive;" and "It is not possible to take the square root of a negative number."

4 Discussing Rules

Have a class discussion about the rules students came up with for square and cube roots and positive and negative numbers. These questions may be helpful in your discussion:

- What different rules did you come up with?
- What numbers did you use to discover your rule?
- Are there any counterexamples for this rule that were overlooked?
- Why do you think that your rule is true for many numbers and not just a few specific examples?

student page

5 Writing and Revising a Mathematical Argument

Before students write their own mathematical arguments about the relationship between the size of a given cube number and the size of its original number, point out the questions from Guidelines for Writing Your Own Mathematical Argument on Student Guide page 19 or Reproducible R12. After students have finished, ask them to trade their mathematical arguments with partners for feedback. Then have students return the mathematical arguments and comments to their partners so that they can make revisions based on the feedback.

👆 Throughout the unit, students will write arguments, trade them with partners for feedback, and make revisions. If students are not used to giving feedback on each other's work, suggest writing prompts such as these: "In your mathematical argument, you do a nice job of . . . ;" "Things that I think you could improve are . . . ;" and "I don't understand what you mean by . . . ." One way students could revise the rule is: "The cube of any number greater than 1 is always larger than the original number."

what to look for

DO STUDENTS' MATHEMATICAL ARGUMENTS:

- *show an understanding of cube numbers and cube roots?*
- *clearly state a rule about the relationship of the size of cube numbers to the original number?*
- *describe methods used to figure out the rule and include counterexamples?*
- *include an explanation of special cases for which the rule does not work?*

See *Making Mathematical Arguments* Assessment page A9 for assessment information.

Square and cube roots
a. $16 = 2^3$ $(2×2×2)$
b. $25 = 2^2$ $(2×2)$
c. can't find one
d. $25 = (-5)^2$ $(-5·-5)$
e. can't find one
f. can't find one
g. $-8 = (-2)^3$
h. can't find one

Writing and revising a Mathematical Argument

The cube of any number except 0, 1, negatives, or fractions is always larger than the original number.

I tried different numbers and I found 0, 1, & negatives do not work. I also tried fractions and they didn't work.

Special Cases	
original number	cube number
0	0
1	1
-2	-8
$\frac{1}{4}$	$\frac{1}{64}$

...continue needed in my...

Look at Square and Cube Roots

As you answer the questions below, think about rules you might make.

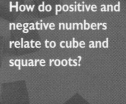

How do positive and negative numbers relate to cube and square roots?

1 Can you find each of these numbers? If you can, give an example. If you cannot, write "no."

  a. positive cube number with a positive cube root
  b. positive square number with a positive square root
  c. positive cube number with a negative cube root
  d. positive square number with a negative square root
  e. negative cube number with a positive cube root
  f. negative square number with a positive square root
  g. negative cube number with a negative cube root
  h. negative square number with a negative square root

2 What rules can you come up with for square and cube roots and positive and negative numbers? Why do your rules work?

Write and Revise a Mathematical Argument

Follow these steps to write and revise your own mathematical argument about cube numbers and original numbers.

1 Write a mathematical argument that includes a statement of the basic rule or mathematical idea, the methods used to figure out the rule, and any counterexamples you found where your rule did not work. Be sure to include a description of what happens in special cases.

2 Trade mathematical arguments with a partner. Look at the handout Guidelines for Writing Your Own Mathematical Argument.

  a. Did your partner meet all of the guidelines?

  b. Is there information in your partner's argument that you don't understand?

  c. Is there information you think your partner left out?

3 Revise your mathematical argument using your partner's feedback and any other information you have learned.

hot **words**   cubic numbers
  cubic roots

Hme**work**
page 40

Writing About a Pattern

To save time, I gave students The Powers Chart with the numbers already filled in. That way the students could just focus on finding the perfect squares and thinking about the patterns. □

A Powerful Argument

student page

1 Creating a Powers Chart

Before students copy the chart, make sure that they understand how to fill in the first row by going over it together with the class. For information about how to use a calculator to square and cube a number, see page 35. To raise a number to a power higher than 3, let students know they can continue to press the $=$ button. Then have students complete the rest of the chart on their own.

The main purpose of this investigation is to find the perfect squares in the chart rather than finding powers of a number. As students search for perfect squares, some interesting patterns emerge. The x^2, x^4, and x^6 columns all are perfect squares, as well as the rows for 1, 4, and 9. See Math Background, page 34, for a more information. See Assessment page A28 for a completely filled in chart.

2 Discussing the Patterns

As you lead the class discussion, help students think about why the perfect squares appear where they do. This discussion is intended to help students describe relationships they notice that exist between the columns or rows. During the discussion, you might want students to draw cubes or arrange cubes to see the patterns.

- What columns or rows have perfect squares in them? Why do you think this is?

- What do you think the next column or row of perfect squares would be? Why?

- It is easy to see why 4^2 is a perfect square. Why is 4^3 also a perfect square? Why is 5^4 a perfect square?

- Can you state a general rule about the rows that will have perfect squares in them? (Answer: If you start with a perfect square and raise it to any power, the result will be a perfect square.)

hot **topics**

• *Powers and Exponents*
• *Length and Distance*

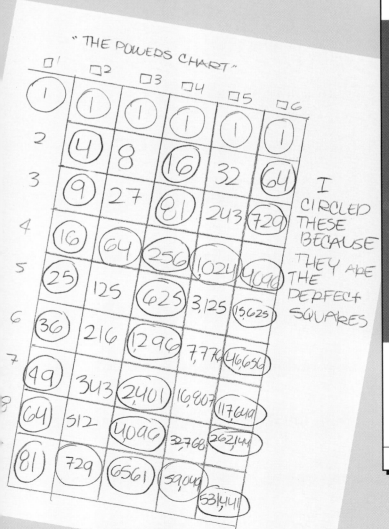

"THE POWERS CHART"

8 A Powerful Argument

WRITING A
MATHEMATICAL
ARGUMENT
ABOUT A PATTERN

In this lesson, you will search for perfect squares in a chart which has numbers raised from the power of 2 to the power of 6. Exploring patterns in the location of these perfect squares helps you understand more about squares, roots, and exponents. This will prepare you for writing your own mathematical argument about one of the patterns.

Create a Powers Chart

What patterns of perfect squares can you find in The Powers Chart?

Make a chart like the one shown and follow the next three steps.

The Powers Chart

	$\square^1$	$\square^2$	$\square^3$	$\square^4$	$\square^5$	$\square^6$
1	1					
2	2					
3	3					
4	4					
5	5					
6	6					
7	7					
8	8					
9	9					

1 Use your calculator to fill in the chart by raising each number to the exponent shown at the top of the column.

2 When you have filled in all the numbers, use your calculator to check which numbers are perfect squares and circle them.

3 Do you see any patterns in the rows and columns where numbers are circled?

By the time students got to writing their mathematical arguments, they understood raising 0 and 1 to the different exponents, but were having some problem with the fractions. I told them to put the calculators away and just do the basic math on a sheet of scratch paper. This helped—they were able to practice the multiplication and continue to progress to the fourth and fifth power of a fraction with ease. As long as they didn't make simple calculation errors, they were able to complete their charts. □

student page

3 Writing a Mathematical Argument

Before students begin writing their own mathematical arguments, you might want to revisit the question: What are the characteristics of a good mathematical argument? Be explicit with students about what should be included. You might need to point out the Guidelines for Writing Your Own Mathematical Argument on Reproducible R12 or Student Guide page 19.

By this point in the unit, students have worked with four special cases: 0, 1, fractions, and negative numbers. You probably want students to realize on their own that they should explore these special cases. One possible mathematical argument that students may write is: "If you raise any whole number except 0 to an even power, the result will be a perfect square."

student page

4 Testing and Revising a Mathematical Argument

As students test each other's mathematical arguments, make sure they have the Guidelines for Writing Your Own Mathematical Argument handy. Allow ample time for students to revise their own mathematical arguments based on feedback from their partners.

DO STUDENTS' MATHEMATICAL ARGUMENTS:

- *show an understanding of the patterns of perfect squares found on the grid?*
- *clearly state a rule about the patterns of perfect squares that appear in rows or columns of the grid?*
- *describe methods used to figure out the rule and include counterexamples?*
- *include an explanation of special cases for which the rule does not work?*

See *Making Mathematical Arguments* Assessment page A5 for assessment information.

Write a Mathematical Argument

"If you raise any number to an even power, the result will be a perfect square."

Methods

$0^2 = 0$

I looked at My partners. My partner was cheryce.

partner does make sense because information she gave me was right.

I understand all the information she gave Me.

3. She wrote all the information needed.

Write a Mathematical Argument

We have talked about a rule for the pattern found in the rows of the Powers Chart. This statement describes the pattern found in the columns of the chart: "If you raise any number to an even power, the result will be a perfect square."

1 Test the statement above and revise it by using the handout Guidelines for Writing Your Own Mathematical Argument.

2 Remember to include a statement of the basic rule, the methods used to figure out the rule and any counterexamples, and a description of what happens with special cases.

How would you write a mathematical argument about one of the patterns?

Test and Revise a Mathematical Argument

Work with a partner who will provide feedback and revise your mathematical argument by completing the following:

- Trade mathematical arguments with a partner.

- Read your partner's argument, checking to be sure your partner responded well to all of the questions in the Guidelines for Writing Your Own Mathematical Argument. Look for anything you don't understand and or anything your partner might have left out, and write down your comments.

- Return the mathematical argument and comments to your partner.

- Make revisions to your mathematical argument based on the written comments you receive from your partner.

hot words | even number
perfect square

Homework

page 41

MAKING MATHEMATICAL ARGUMENTS LESSON 8
© Creative Publications • MathScape **23**

A TEACHER REFLECTS

Understanding How to Write Mathematical Arguments

In Lesson 5, determining whether the rule students wrote for predicting the increase for any perfect square would work for the negative square root was challenging for some of my students. It was as if the patterns activity previously had distracted them because they had a difficult time understanding the square root sign. Some could instantly follow the logic and "see" that the square root of 100 could be negative or positive. Others looked at me as if they had just been introduced to college trigonometry. For these students, it was "back to the drawing board." I started them over with the explanation of multiplying signed numbers. They told me the rules, and we continued from there.

Students thought that Dan's Mathematical Argument in Lesson 6 made sense and could quickly compute the squares. When they were asked to find counterexamples, it didn't dawn on them to check negative numbers or fractions. Once I suggested it to one or two students, others tried more challenging examples.

When I asked students to share their methods, they struggled with showing fractional representation on the overhead. I had to model one problem so they understood what I was asking them to do. I asked for a volunteer to give me a fraction and Brenda gave me $\frac{1}{4}$. I then asked the class what to do to square it. Many hands shot up and Jackie told us to multiply 1 times 1 for the numerator and 4 times 4 to get the denominator. When I asked them which was larger—$\frac{1}{4}$ or $\frac{1}{16}$—many picked $\frac{1}{16}$. We voted and the class was split—half insisted that $\frac{1}{16}$ was larger. I introduced the pizza problem—would you rather have $\frac{1}{4}$ or $\frac{1}{16}$ of the pizza? Which piece is larger? The concept began to catch on, and the students visualized and modeled $\frac{1}{4}$ as larger than $\frac{1}{16}$. When they created their own examples, most students opted to use fraction segments of a square (instead of the traditional circle). Once students were moving freely on finding counterexamples and special cases, few struggled with revising Dan's Mathematical Argument.

Primes, Patterns, and Generalizations

Students look for patterns of primes and factors, then pull together what they have learned in the unit to make a mathematical argument about a pattern of their choice.

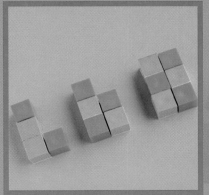

LESSON 9

Three-Stack Shape Sums

Students examine a rule about divisibility that describes the sum of three consecutive integers. Using cubes, students build the numbers 1–15 according to the 3-stack model and record their findings. To investigate why the sum of three consecutive integers is always divisible by 3, students create a table and draw conclusions from the table. Students write and revise mathematical arguments about divisibility so that they are always true.

Mathematical Goals

- Gain familiarity with the 3-stack model for representing numbers.

- Relate a visual model for finding factors to divisibility.

- Draw conclusions about the sum of two numbers and use them as a basis for understanding the sum of three consecutive integers.

- Write and understand a mathematical argument about divisibility.

MATERIALS

PER STUDENT

- calculator

- Reproducible R13

PER PAIR

- 15 Rainbow Centimeter Cubes

PREPARATION

Read Math Background, page 56, to familiarize yourself with why the sum of any three consecutive integers is always divisible by 3.

LESSON 10

A Stretching Problem

Students use a script about a bubble gum factory to explore prime numbers, factors, and multiples. Students learn about prime factorization as they find which combinations of stretching machines would be needed to stretch certain lengths of bubble gum. At the end of the lesson, students write mathematical arguments about prime numbers.

MATERIALS

PER STUDENT

- calculator

- Reproducibles R14–R15

Mathematical Goals

- Identify the prime numbers from 1 to 100.

- Think about factors and multiples to find patterns of numbers that are composite.

- Find the prime factorization of a number.

- Identify all the factors of a number.

LESSON 11

Pattern Appearances

How many times will each of the numbers 1–25 appear on the Multiplication Chart? As students record their results, some interesting patterns emerge involving squares, cubes, primes, and factors. Students form their own theories about the numbers that appear two times, three times, four times, and more. Students use what they learn about the patterns in the Multiplication Chart to write their final mathematical arguments in the next lesson.

Mathematical Goals

- Search for patterns and make and test predictions based on those patterns.

- Describe general rules derived from patterns.

- Recognize perfect squares, perfect cubes, and primes.

- Find all the factors of a number.

MATERIALS

PER STUDENT

- calculator

- Reproducible R16

PREPARATION

Students will need the table they create in this lesson for their Lessons 11 and 12 homework assignments.

LESSON 12

The Final Arguments

In this lesson, which is both an assessment lesson and a continuation of the previous lesson, students write their final mathematical argument about the patterns they found in the Multiplication Chart. In small groups, students discuss what they will write their mathematical arguments about. Then each student writes a mathematical argument, gives it to a partner for feedback, and revises it based on the partner's feedback.

Mathematical Goals

- Write a complete mathematical argument from scratch that includes a rule and its mathematical boundaries.

- Check for special cases in the mathematical argument.

- Find patterns in factors, primes, squares, or cubes.

MATERIALS

PER STUDENT

- calculator

PREPARATION

Make sure students have the following from Lesson 11: the Multiplication Chart (R16), the table that they created, and their writing from Step 5. They will need the table for homework in this lesson.

MATH BACKGROUND

Divisibility

In Lesson 9, students are introduced to divisibility, with a focus on divisibility by 3. This lesson begins by posing a problem to students that has a very surprising result. The lesson then develops into an exploration of the logical reasons behind the result. Understanding that a whole number is divisible by another whole number if, when it is divided by that number, the result is a whole number, students arrange cubes to explore why the sum of any three consecutive whole numbers is always divisible by 3. First, students learn how to make numbers using "3-stacks" as shown below.

Students informally categorize numbers they make with the 3-stack model as either a rectangle number (which is any multiple of 3), an L number (which is a rectangle + 1 and includes 1, 4, 7, any 1 mod 3 number…), or a b number (which is a rectangle + 2). Then they respond to questions,

such as: What pairs of numbers added together will result in a rectangle number? a b number? an L number? Why is it that you can add any three consecutive numbers together and get a number that is divisible by 3?

Students are actually working with the number-theory premise that any number can be expressed as $3n$, $3n + 1$, or $3n + 2$, although they are not required to use variables in the investigation. The modeling that they do with cubes and articulate in informal language can also be expressed in this algebraic equation: $(n - 1) + n + (n + 1) = 3n$. The use of cubes in this investigation demonstrates the power of mathematical modeling tools to make sophisticated mathematical concepts accessible to students.

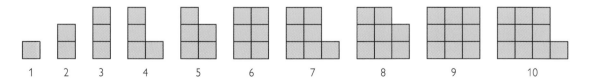

Generalizing About Patterns

The focus in Phase Two was on testing a rule for special cases. Lessons 11 and 12 focus on students' ability to identify a pattern to use as a basis for a rule, as well as understand and articulate why they know a rule is true beyond just giving examples. In Lesson 11, students create a table showing the frequency of a number on the Multiplication Chart (see Reproducible R16). The number of times a number appears in the Multiplication Chart is the same as the number of factors it has. If students do not figure this out by the end of Lesson 11, they may have noticed a number of other things that may help them see the connection to factors. For example, all the numbers in the 2-times column are prime numbers. The numbers in the 3-times column are all perfect squares of prime numbers. The numbers in the 4-times column are either perfect cubes (though not all the perfect cubes belong in this column) or products of two primes.

Developing Strong Mathematical Arguments

By Lesson 12, students are able to find an interesting pattern (or possible pattern) and experiment with it. The interplay of patterns involving the occurrence of squares, cubes, primes, factors, and multiples that appears in the Multiplication Chart and the skills students have developed in making mathematical arguments make for a rich assessment opportunity at the end of the unit. Students bring all they have learned together to craft a mathematical argument of their own choosing about a pattern they have noticed involving one or more of these different categories of numbers.

Three-Stack Shape Sums

Have students review the phase overview on pages 24–25 in the Student Guide.

I encouraged students to describe the number 5, for example, as having 2 extra little squares rather than having one square missing in the corner. I suggested that they think of what is shown in the number, rather than what is missing. This kept the model consistent with looking at addition—how much is added on the number—rather than what is missing, or subtracted from the number. □

1 Discussing the Mathematical Statement

Using the questions below, ask the class to think about whether or not this statement is true: "The sum of three consecutive integers is divisible by 3." Encourage students to try several examples before answering each question. Do not let students know that this statement is always true now because they will be showing this in their mathematical arguments at the end of the lesson.

- Choose any three consecutive whole numbers and add them. Can you divide your answer by 3 evenly?

- Can you find three consecutive whole numbers whose sum is not evenly divisible by 3?

2 Creating Numbers Using the Three-stack Model

Distribute cubes to students, and Centimeter Grid Paper, Reproducible R13, to each student. Demonstrate to the class how to make several series of three consecutive numbers, such as 4, 5, and 6, with cubes using the 3-stack model shown in the Student Guide. Let students know that they should build cubes up in a column until the column is 3 cubes high. Then they start on a new column to the right and build that column until

it is 3 cubes high, and so on. During the investigation students will be using cubes to make one number at a time and recording the number on grid paper.

3 Looking at Different Kinds of Numbers

Bring the class together to discuss the patterns students found. Use the terms L numbers, b numbers, and rectangle numbers to describe the patterns students identify. Questions like the following can help students move from smaller numbers they can model with cubes or find by extending their tables to larger numbers that require more abstract reasoning.

- What kind of a number is 18? 23? 28? 31? 36?

- What kind of a number is 1? 2?

- What are three other rectangle numbers that are larger than 100? L numbers that are larger than 200? b numbers that are larger than 300?

- How can you tell whether a number is a rectangle number, an L number, or a b number without building it?

Use cubes to demonstrate to students that the sides of a rectangle number are the factors of the number and that all of these rectangle numbers have a factor of 3. See Math Background, page 56, for more information about divisibility.

hot **topics**

• *Factors and Multiples*
• *Counterexamples*

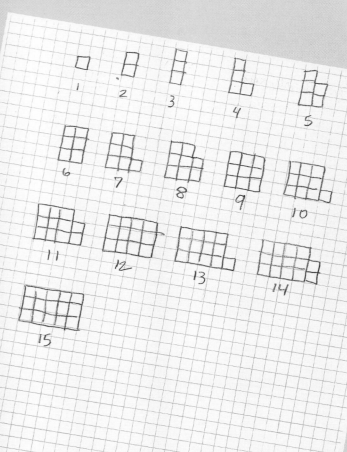

9 Three-Stack Shape Sums

INVESTIGATING
A PATTERN IN
DIVISIBILITY BY 3

In the last phase, you used cubes to model square numbers. In this lesson, you model numbers by organizing cubes into stacks of three. Looking at numbers modeled in this way will help you investigate the statement: "The sum of any three consecutive whole numbers will always be divisible by 3."

Create Numbers Using the 3-Stacks Model

What patterns can you see when you make numbers with the 3-stacks model?

We say that one number is divisible by a second number if the first number can be divided evenly by the second number, leaving a remainder of 0. With the class, you have tried to see if you could find any three consecutive whole numbers whose sum is not evenly divisible by 3. Work with a partner and follow the investigation steps below to explore some patterns in consecutive numbers.

1 Use cubes to make each number from 1 to 15 following the 3-stacks model. On grid paper, record each number like the numbers shown in How to Use the 3-Stacks Model.

2 Look for patterns in the way the numbers look in the 3-stacks model. Be ready to describe any patterns you notice.

How to Use the 3-Stacks Model

L Number	b Number	Rectangle Number
L	b	
4	5	6

Each time you have a stack of three cubes, start on a new column to the right.

MAKING MATHEMATICAL ARGUMENTS   LESSON 9
26   © Creative Publications • MathScape

I encouraged students to approach this investigation in their own way. Some wanted to try specific numbers, and others wanted to focus on the 3-stack model. I gave students who were having difficulty a few specific examples to try, such as 9 + 13 for a "rectangle + L" example. I helped students see the connection to the 3-stack model. I noticed the table included examples that reinforce the commutative property, such as rectangle + L and L + rectangle. I did not assume that students necessarily saw these as the same. □

student page

4 Investigating the Sum of Numbers

Before students begin making the table, you might want to list a few of the possible combinations with the class. Make sure students understand that the 3-stack model of adding means that they can put two shapes together and add the areas. Shapes can be reoriented, turned, and flipped, but they retain the same area.

5 Analyzing the Tables

As the class discusses the tables, focus on explanations of "How did you figure this out?" or "How do you know?" This is the preparation for making a mathematical argument in the next step. Use questions such as the following:

- What are some different pairs of numbers you can add together to get a rectangle number sum? an L number sum? a b number sum?

- How can you fit an L number together with a b number to get a rectangle number?

- How can you predict which kind of number a sum of two numbers will be?

- How can you use the model to explain what happens when you add three consecutive whole numbers?

This last question is important because it focuses students back to the overall question for the lesson: Why is the sum of three consecutive whole numbers divisible by 3? Make sure students come away with the understanding that whenever you put together a b number and an L number, you get a rectangle number. A rectangle number put together with another rectangle number is a rectangle number. 3-stack rectangles all have a factor of 3, which means they are divisible by 3.

student page

6 Writing and Revising a Mathematical Argument

As students write their arguments, remind them of the Guidelines for Writing Your Own Mathematical Argument. The only special cases students can check for are integers (0, 1, and negative numbers) because the statement says the numbers must be consecutive. The rule cannot be applied to fractions because the notion of "consecutive fractions" does not make sense: there is no limit to the number of fractions that are between any two numbers. Students should find that the rule is always true as originally stated.

* show an understanding of why the sum of any
  three consecutive integers will always be divisible
  by 3?
* clearly state a rule about the divisibility of the
  sum of any three consecutive integers?
* describe methods used to figure out the rule and
  include counterexamples?
* include an explanation of special cases for which
  the rule does not work?

**See _Making Mathematical Arguments_
Assessment page A13 for assessment
information.**

Investigate the Sum of Numbers

In the last investigation, you found that numbers you made with
cubes in the 3-stacks model could be described as L numbers, b
numbers, or rectangle numbers. Follow the steps below to think
about what it means to add any two kinds of numbers.

1 Make a table like the one shown. Put all the possible
combinations of L numbers, b numbers, and rectangle
numbers you can think of in the first two columns.

2 Then think about what your result would be if you added
these kinds of numbers. Put that information in the third
column.

3 What conclusions can you make about the sum of two
numbers by looking at your table?

> How can you predict
> whether the sum
> of two numbers will
> be an L number,
> a b number, or a
> rectangle number?

If you add this kind of number:	to this kind of number:	you get this kind of number:

Write and Revise a Mathematical Argument

Through class discussion, you have learned that a whole number
is divisible by its factors. Write your own mathematical argument
for this statement: "Whenever you add three consecutive whole
numbers together, the sum will be divisible by 3."

* Remember to check your thinking. Are there any special cases
  you should consider? What happens with each of the special
  cases?

* Trade your argument with a partner and ask your partner
  to comment on it.

* Revise your mathematical argument based on your
  partner's comments.

hot **words** | factors
mathematical argument

Homework

page 42

10

Generalizing About Factors, Multiples, and Primes

The script idea in this lesson was fantastic! What a great change of pace from the usual math. Everyone wanted to volunteer to read a role. I put The Bubble Gum Factory handout on an overhead to conserve paper and we read through the roles. After students had crossed off the unnecessary machines on the Unnecessary Machines handout, I had students take out another sheet of paper and make a chart to show why they crossed out the machines. This prompted them to do more mathematical thinking and justify their responses. Students were held accountable for crossing out the unnecessary machines. □

A Stretching Problem

1 Discussing the Script

After students have read how the Bubble Gum Factory works in the Student Guide, distribute The Bubble Gum Factory Script, Reproducible R14. You might want to have the script read aloud by a few students who have been assigned the different parts. This script introduces the problem for this lesson. In the context of a bubble gum factory crisis, students will be using factors and multiples to help them find prime numbers and will be finding the prime factors of numbers. Questions such as the following can help students understand the script before they begin the investigation in the next step:

- How do the stretching machines work?

- Explain in your own words why machine 22 was not necessary.

- What other machines do you think the factory could do without?

2 Finding the Unnecessary Machines

Before students begin the investigation, distribute The Unnecessary Machines, Reproducible R15. Be sure they understand the directions in the Student Guide and realize that each square repre-sents one machine in the Bubble Gum Factory. After students cross off any of the machines that they decide are unnecessary, the machines that are left will be the 25 prime numbers between 1 and 100.

Students sometimes mistakenly believe that particular numbers, such as 51, 87, or 91, are prime, because they somehow "look" prime, or because students do not know divisibility rules. If students are having difficulty, suggest that they try going through the chart counting by 3's, 4's, etc., and finding the multiples of those numbers. Students should find that the prime numbers are: 2, 3, 5, 7, 11, 13, 17, 19, 23, 29, 31, 37, 41, 43, 47, 53, 59, 61, 67, 71, 73, 79, 83, 89, and 97.

3 Discussing Ways to Find Unnecessary Machines

Help the class generate a list of different ways to rule out the unnecessary machines. As students describe their different methods, encourage them to use the terms *factor, multiple,* and *prime* where appropriate. This step can serve as a review of these concepts for students.

- What methods did you use for finding the unnecessary machines?

- What patterns did you notice in the numbers of the unnecessary machines?

- What were some general rules you used so that you didn't need to look at every machine?

hot topics

- *Factors and Multiples*
- *Perimeter*

THE UNNECESSARY MACHINES

---

10 A Stretching Problem

GENERALIZING
ABOUT FACTORS,
MULTIPLES,
AND PRIMES

A prime number is a number that has exactly two factors, 1 and itself. In this lesson, you will be looking at patterns in prime numbers to solve a problem at a bubble gum factory. Then you will write your own mathematical argument about prime numbers.

Find the Unnecessary Machines

How can factors and multiples help you think about prime numbers?

First, read the information on this page about the Bubble Gum Factory to understand how it operates. Then read the handout The Bubble Gum Factory Script to find out what problem you can solve for the Bubble Gum Factory.

1 Look at the handout The Unnecessary Machines. Each one of the squares on The Unnecessary Machines is one of the machines in the Bubble Gum Factory. Some of the machines are unnecessary because combinations of other machines could be used instead.

2 Figure out which machines are actually unnecessary and cross them off. Be prepared to discuss with the class why you crossed off these machines.

The Bubble Gum Factory

At the Bubble Gum Factory, 1-inch lengths of gum are stretched to lengths from 1 inch to 100 inches by putting them through a stretching machine. There are 100 stretching machines. Machine 23, for example, will stretch a piece of gum to 23 times its original length.

I shared with the class some of the prime number problems that remain unsolved: Is every even integer greater than 4 a sum of two odd primes (The Goldback Conjecture)? Is there an infinite number of primes p for which p + 2 is also prime (The Twin Prime Problem)? □

Some of the stronger mathematicians in my classes were talking about the bubble gum machines. One student said, "Once you cross off machine 10, you can't use it for machine 20. You can only use the ones you haven't crossed out yet." Another student questioned, "Can you put the gum through more than two machines? I think you have to use these to substitute for machine 20: 5 × 2 × 2. I know that's right." As I was passing by a group of students, I overheard one student in the group telling her tablemates, "Remember those factoring trees with prime numbers that we did last year? It's just like that." Yes! They made the connection and used mathematical terminology! □

student page

4 Investigating the Necessary Machines

As students think about how they could combine the necessary machines to get other lengths, they are learning about prime factorization. This concept will be discussed in the next step. See Assessment page A28 for solutions to this investigation.

5 Discussing Prime Factorization

After students have completed the investigation, have a class discussion on prime factorization using questions such as those below. Make sure students understand that the necessary machines correspond to the prime numbers.

- What do you notice about the necessary machines? Are they prime numbers? Why or why not?

- How can you tell if a number is prime?

- Can you write any number as the product of numbers that are prime? Explain your thinking.

The idea behind prime factorization is that any whole number greater than 1 can be written as the product of prime factors. It is not necessary to explain this now because students will be testing it out when they write their mathematical argument in the next step.

student page

6 Writing and Revising a Mathematical Argument

Before students begin to write their own arguments, spend a few minutes discussing the fact that the following statement does not apply for all special cases: "Any number can be written as the product of prime factors." For example, since proper fractions are not whole numbers, they cannot be expressed as products of primes, which are always whole numbers. Encourage students to look for other special cases. They need not stick to the four cases from the previous phase. Help students understand that their mathematical arguments should define the range of numbers for which the rule is true; considering special cases is a way of thinking about that.

Remind students to use Guidelines for Writing Your Own Mathematical Argument if necessary. For this mathematical argument, the special cases 0, 1, fractions, and negative numbers do not apply. Students should eventually identify the range of numbers that fit this rule as positive integers greater than 1.

DO STUDENTS' MATHEMATICAL ARGUMENTS:

- show an understanding of prime numbers and prime factorization?
- clearly state a rule about prime numbers?
- describe methods used to figure out the rule and include counterexamples?
- include an explanation of special cases for which the rule does not work?

See Making Mathematical Arguments Assessment page A13 for assessment information.

Investigate
necessary
machines

1. What machines would you use to get the lengths:

15 = 5, 3
28 = 7, 2, 2
36 = 2, 3, 3, 2
65 = 13, 5
84 =

at length of bubblegum would
eed to go through the most number
of necessary machines? How did
you figure out your answer?

64

Because it need's to go
through the number
2 six times.

Investigate the Necessary Machines

Use the questions below to find out how you could combine the *necessary* machines to get other lengths. Any of these machines may be used more than once to give the requested length.

What prime numbers can you use to make other numbers?

1 What machines would be necessary to get the lengths: 15? 28? 36? 65? 84?

2 For each of the lengths above, what other machines could have been used that were unnecessary?

3 Which lengths between 1 and 100 would come out if the bubble gum went through five machines and all 5 machines were necessary ones?

4 Which length between 1 and 100 requires the greatest number of necessary machines? How did you figure out your answer?

Write and Revise a Mathematical Argument

Write your own mathematical argument about this statement: "Any number can be written as the product of prime factors."

- Consider all the special cases we have used in this unit. Think about whether the special cases should be included in your argument. If a special case does not apply, it is sufficient to say so in your mathematical argument.

- Look for special cases other than 0, 1, proper fractions, and negative numbers. Your mathematical argument should describe the range of numbers for which the rule is true.

- Work with a partner to read and comment on each other's arguments.

- Revise your mathematical argument based on your partner's comments.

hot words | factors
prime number

Homework
page 43

MAKING MATHEMATICAL ARGUMENTS LESSON 10
© Creative Publications • MathScape **29**

Pattern Appearances

Some of my students got a little confused when I asked them how many times 16 would appear on the chart, since 1 × 16 is not shown. They were not sure whether they were supposed to count a number if it did not physically appear on the chart. So we listed the pairs we had found: 16 × 1, 8 × 2, 4 × 4, and 2 × 8. Many students then saw the symmetry and said that 1 × 16 would be another pair. One student asked, "Are we pretending the paper is bigger?" I said, "Yes," and explained that while the paper was limited, they should think of all the possible times a number would appear if the paper were larger. We all tried 24 together, and by then, students were catching on. □

1 Finding Out How Often 1–10 Appear

After distributing the Multiplication Chart, Reproducible R16, explain to students that this chart shows the products of the numbers in each row and column. On the chalkboard, draw a table like the one shown on the next page with the same column headings, but without data. Record data in the table by asking students how many times the numbers 1–10 appear on the chart. Have students create and fill in their own tables on blank paper. This lesson focuses on how students can reliably predict which column of the table a number will appear in.

2 Discussing the Chart

Ask students the questions below to help them understand that they will be looking for how many times a number would appear on the Multiplication Chart if the chart were expanded, not just how many times it appears on the chart that they have.

- How many times would 26 appear on the chart if it were expanded? (Answer: 26 would appear 4 times, even though only two 26's appear on the Multiplication Chart.)

- How many times would 50 appear on the chart if it were expanded? (Answer: 50 would appear 6 times, even though only two 50's appear on the Multiplication Chart.)

3 Finding Out How Often 11–25 Appear

Ask, "How can you find out the number of times any number will appear on an expanded chart?" and explain that they will be trying to figure out a way to do this in this lesson. Have students figure out how many times 11–25 would appear on the chart, so that they have more values in their tables on which to base some hypotheses. When students have finished, suggest that small groups get together to compare their answers and see if they agree on their answers.

As students fill out their tables, they will start to form ideas about which kinds of numbers appear in which columns. For instance, after completing 1–10, students may think that the perfect squares are all going to appear in the 3-times column. However, 16 does not fall in this column, while 25 does. This surprise encourages students to look for other less obvious explanations.

How many times will a number appear on the multiplication chart?

1x	2x	3x	4x	5x	6x	7x	8x	9x	10x
1	2	4	16	12			24		
	3	6		18					
	5	8		20					
	7	10							
	25	14							
		15							
		21							
		22							
11									
13									
17									
19									
23									

11 Pattern Appearances

GENERALIZING
ABOUT PATTERNS IN
A MULTIPLICATION
CHART

You will continue to think about squares, cubes, primes, and factors as you look for patterns in the Multiplication Chart. From these patterns you can make some general rules. Your goal will be to find out how many times any number would appear in the Multiplication Chart if the chart continued into infinity!

How many times will 11–25 appear on the Multiplication Chart?

Find Out How Often Numbers 11–25 Appear

After you work with the class to find out how many times the numbers 1–10 appear on the handout Multiplication Chart, expand your investigation by responding to the directions below. You will need the table you made with the class for this investigation.

1 How many times will 11 appear on the chart? 12? 13? Figure out how many times each of the numbers from 11 to 25 would appear on the chart and add them to your table. Remember to include how many times the number would appear if the chart went on into infinity, not just the number of times it appears on the Multiplication Chart you have.

2 Do you have any ideas about how you might predict the number of times any number will appear on the chart?

Multiplication Chart

×	1	2	3	4	5	6	7	8	9	10	1
1	1	2	3	4	5	6	7	8	9	10	1
2	2	4	6	8	10	12	14	16	18	20	2
3	3	6	9	12	15	18	21	24	27	30	3
4	4	8	12	16	20	24	28	32	36	40	4
5	5	10	15	20	25	30	35	40	45	50	5
	6	12	18	24	30	36	42	48	54	60	6

MAKING MATHEMATICAL ARGUMENTS LESSON 11
30 © Creative Publications • MathScape

Many students instantly noticed the pattern and could predict which columns certain numbers would appear in depending on the number of factors. I found it helpful to expand the Multiplication Chart to 20 × 20 for a few of my students so that they could actually check their answers and make sure the answers were correct. Some students were instantly cluing into the "perfect squares" and "perfect cubes." They could be overheard sharing their information with other classmates. From that point, all the students saw the patterns with more ease. □

4 Predicting in Which Column a Number Belongs

Before students begin the investigation in the Student Guide, ask them the following questions and have a class discussion based on their answers so that they will be prepared for the rest of the investigation.

- What ideas do you have at this point about predicting which column a number will go in? Write down a couple of your theories and why you think they might be true.

- In which column of your table do you think each of these numbers belongs: 27? 36? 37? 42?

- Make a list of the four numbers, and what column you predicted for each one. Then check your prediction on the Multiplication Chart, and write down which column the number actually belongs in on your table. Which numbers did you predict correctly?

5 Generalizing About the Column in Which Any Number Belongs

Encourage students to participate in a class discussion by responding the following questions:

- What did you notice about the numbers in different columns?

- Can you predict another number that would belong in the 2-times column? the 3-times column? in other columns?

- How would you predict which column *any* number belongs in?

After the discussion ask students to write their generalizations about which column of their table any number on the Multiplication Chart belongs in. This will help students as they write their own mathematical arguments in the next lesson. Be sure students save their writing from this step, the tables they made in this lesson, and the Multiplication Chart for the next lesson.

Some students may not have figured out that the number of times a number appears in an expanded multiplication chart is the same as the number of factors it has. See Math Background, page 57, for more information that you can use to help students see the connection to factors. If this information comes up in the discussion here, help students think about how it is related to the number of factors.

what to look for

DO STUDENTS' PREDICTIONS:

- *describe patterns that they found?*
- *show an understanding of what perfect squares, perfect cubes, and primes are?*
- *show an understanding of how to find all the factors of a number?*
- *describe general rules based on patterns?*

See Making Mathematical Arguments Assessment page A13 for assessment information.

1. #

50	column
28	6x
99	6x
87	6x
40	4x
	8x

a. All the numbers in the "2x" column are prime numbers.

b. All the numbers in the "3x" column are perfect squares of prime numbers.

c. The numbers in the 4x column are all perfect cubes or two primes' products.

2.a. One number that can be put in the "2x" column is the number 53.

b. One number that belongs in the "3x" column is the number 49.

c. A number that belong in the "4x" column is the number 33.

Generalize About the Column which any Number Belongs

You can put any number in a column by how many factors the number has (ex. The number 8 has 4 factors [1,8,2,4] which means you put it in the "4x column.

Predict in Which Column a Number Belongs

You will need the table you made for this investigation. After exploring with the class which columns of your table the numbers 27, 36, 37, and 42 belong in, answer the questions below.

How can you predict which column of your table a number belongs in?

1 Choose five other numbers of your own between 26 and 100. What columns of your table do you think they belong in? Use the Multiplication Chart to check your predictions and then write the numbers in the appropriate columns on your table.

a. How would you describe the numbers that appear in the 2-times column of your table?

b. How would you describe the numbers that appear in the 3-times column of your table?

c. Choose one other column of your table. How would you describe the numbers that appear in that column?

2 Identify numbers that belong in particular columns of your table.

a. Can you think of a number that belongs in the 2-times column that is not already there? Write it in the column on your table.

b. Can you think of a number that belongs in the 3-times column that is not already there? Write it in the column on your table.

c. Can you think of a number that belongs in the column you chose in item **1c** that is not already there? Write it in the column on your table.

Generalize About the Column in Which Any Number Belongs

After the class discussion, write an answer to this question: How could you predict which column of your table *any* number would belong in?

- Be sure to include your own thinking about the question.
- Use examples to explain your answer.

hot words | pattern factors

Homework page 44

12

Writing a Complete Mathematical Argument

Most of my students chose one column of their tables for their rules. However, a few of them were able to make more of a generalization. They chose the relationship between the number of factors a number has and the number of times a number would appear in the Multiplication Chart. □

The Final Arguments

1 Reviewing Characteristics of a Good Argument

Review with students the elements of a well-written mathematical argument as shown in the Student Guide. You may want to pose questions such as the following to help students review since they will be assessed on the mathematical arguments they write in this lesson.

- What are some of the things you need to think about when you are deciding whether your rule works or not?

- If you were reading someone else's mathematical argument, what would you look for?

student page ➤

2 Sharing Ideas About Mathematical Arguments

Before students divide into small groups to discuss the topic of their mathematical arguments, remind them that they will not actually write the mathematical arguments until the next step. You could suggest that students might want to take notes, however. Choose one person in the group to be responsible for making sure everyone gets a chance to talk.

☝ The opportunity to talk about what they know before having to write about it is frequently necessary for many middle-school students. The investigation in the Student Guide lists a set of questions students will discuss in their small groups. These questions will help structure what the students write about.

hot topics

- *Factors and Multiples*
- *Statistics*

My rule is the numbers in the 2×
column are all prime numbers. I figured it
out by looking on my column sheet.
The numbers in the 2× colum are
all prime numbers. Prime numbers
are a number that has a factor
itself and one. It works in
cases just if the number is
prime.

12 The Final Arguments

WRITING A
COMPLETE
MATHEMATICAL
ARGUMENT

You will use what you have learned in this unit to write an argument about the numbers in the Multiplication Chart. You will also learn from others as you work together in small groups to share ideas about mathematical arguments.

Share Ideas About Mathematical Arguments

What will you write your mathematical argument about?

Choose something to write your mathematical argument about from the table you made for the handout Multiplication Chart. It could be one of the columns of your table, such as the 2× column, or it could be the numbers that appear most frequently. Your group may choose the same thing, or each person in the group could choose something different.

1 What is your rule for what you chose? How can you state your rule so that anyone who has not done the problem yet will know what you are talking about?

2 Can you find any counterexamples to your rule? If so, how will you change your rule to take them into account?

3 Does your rule work for special cases? Why or why not?

Characteristics of a Good Mathematical Argument

A good mathematical argument should include the following:

- a rule that is general and clearly stated

- a description of how the rule was figured out, including a search for counterexamples (The rule should be revised if any counterexamples are found.)

- a description of special cases to which the rule applies

- a description of why the rule works for some cases and why it doesn't work for other cases

MAKING MATHEMATICAL ARGUMENTS   LESSON 12
32   © Creative Publications • MathScape

Students made their own word banks of applicable mathematics terminology that they might be able to apply to their arguments. When they first started reviewing each other's arguments, they were concentrating on spelling errors. Then I challenged them to find "counterexamples" in the work of their peers, so that they were able to more correctly analyze the arguments. I discussed the mathematical arguments of my ESL students with them orally because it was difficult for them to put their mathematical thoughts into English. □

student page

3 Writing Your Own Mathematical Argument

Ask students to individually write their own mathematical arguments based on the discussion they had in their small groups. Make sure students focus their mathematical arguments on elements of the tables they created for the Multiplication Chart in the previous lesson, such as one of the columns, the numbers occurring least frequently, or the numbers occurring most frequently.

Some students may need some help stating their rules. For those students, you can suggest that their rules be in the form of "All the numbers in the *n*-times column are (what kind of numbers?)." Some possibilities for rules are: "All the numbers in the 2-times column are prime numbers;" "All the numbers in the 3-times column are perfect squares of prime numbers;" "All the numbers in the 4-times column are either perfect cubes or products or two primes;" "The number of times a number appears on the Multiplication Chart is the same as the number of factors the number has;" and "The numbers that occur most frequently are the numbers that have the greatest number of factors."

student page

4 Sharing and Revising Your Mathematical Argument

When students have completed their arguments, ask them to work with a partner to read and comment on each other's arguments. Then have students make changes to their mathematical arguments based on their partners' comments.

You might want to remind students about how to comment on their partners' arguments. Some suggestions are: "In your mathematical argument, you do a nice job of…;" "Things that I think you could improve are…;" and "I don't understand what you mean by…."

On pages 46–48 in the Student Guide, there is a gallery of photographs picturing classroom scenes from the unit.

DO STUDENTS' MATHEMATICAL ARGUMENTS:

- show an understanding of factors, primes, squares, or cubes?
- clearly state a rule about patterns in the Multiplication Chart?
- describe methods used to figure out the rule and include counterexamples?
- include an explanation of special cases for which the rule does not work?

See *Making Mathematical Arguments Assessment* page A13 for assessment information.

Writing a Mathematical Argument

1. Numbers that appear in the "3x" column can only be factored by 3 numbers and are generally squared numbers.

2. I figured this out by going through a multiplication chart from 1 to 100 and looked for numbers that only appear 3 times.

3. As I said, numbers in the "3x" column are squared like 25 (5²) and 49 (7²). Although, some squared numbers like 36 (6²) and 16 (4²) wouldn't go in this column because it can't be factored only 3 times.

x:

25 - 1:5, 5:1, 5:5 goes in "3x" column
36 - 1:36, 36:1, 6:6, 4:9, 9:4, 3:12, 12:3 does not go in "3x" column.

Write Your Own Mathematical Argument

Based on the discussion you had in your group, write your own mathematical argument using the following information:

1 Include all of the Characteristics of a Good Mathematical Argument on page 32.

2 Review the table you created and the Multiplication Chart from Lesson 11. Refer to the writing you did in Lesson 11 about how to predict which column of your table *any* number on the Multiplication Chart would belong in.

What do you include in a well-written mathematical argument?

Share and Revise Your Mathematical Argument

When you have completed your mathematical argument, trade with a partner.

- As you read your partner's argument, think of yourself as a teacher looking for a well-written mathematical argument. Write comments that you think will help your partner improve the argument.

- Use your partner's comments to revise your mathematical argument. Review the Characteristics of a Good Mathematical Argument again to make sure you have included all that is required.

hot **words** | mathematical argument
counterexample

Homework
👥 page 45

MAKING MATHEMATICAL ARGUMENTS   LESSON 12
© Creative Publications • MathScape   **33**

A TEACHER REFLECTS

Evaluating Mathematical Arguments

In Lesson 9, I asked students to explain in words what the terms "consecutive" and "integers" meant. This was beneficial to students who can see math but not necessarily read and understand the terms. Suddenly, they had a more concrete understanding of what the problem was asking them to do. Many students opted to use large consecutive numbers and then made mathematical errors. I provided limitations and had students use three numbers below 30. Stanley was one of the first students to explain the "3" rule to his tablemates. Here is the way he explained it: "If you want to know if a number is divisible by 3, add up the digits. Look at 156. Add the 1 + 5 + 6 and you get 12 and 12 is divisible by 3, so 156 is too!" From this, students were able to conclude that there were no sets of three consecutive numbers that, when added together, would not be divisible by 3.

For Lesson 12, I preferred to have students complete a written evaluation of their partners' mathematical arguments. I suggested that each student complete an evaluation on a sheet of paper that included some points we brainstormed on the overhead. They provided the suggestions for evaluation, and I was able to help "steer" them toward what I was looking for. Still, because they felt that they created the evaluation, they "owned" the evaluation and were more apt to buy into it. They were also able to clearly explain the rules that exist in the Multiplication Chart. This is actually an excellent time to use authentic, alternative assessment methods and have students tell what they know through class presentations using the overhead and student-created posters.

Despite the fact that this unit had progressed for the last month, many ESL students were still struggling with putting their mathematical thoughts into English. This was a challenge for me to try to remedy from a teaching perspective because these students would still have had a hard time if I had adapted the assignment to Spanish because many cannot write in Spanish. One solution which worked well for me was to discuss their answers with these students orally.

Lesson #7

Square & Cube roots

a. $27 = 3^3$ $(3 \times 3 \times 3)$

b. $25 = 2^2$ (2×2)

c. not possible

d. $9 = (-3)^2 = (-3 \cdot -3)$

e. not possible

f. not possible

g. $-27 = (-3)^3$

h. not possible

Write & revised argument

A 5 is related to i
number 125 because
multiply 5×5×5 it will
125, 5's cube numbe

I looked at my partner's paper—

1. My partner did follow directions because she wrote an argument.

2. In my partner's argument I everything that she said. thing that I don't under—

ot to mention which is

A 5 is related to its cube number 125 because if you multiply 5×5×5 it will equal 125, 5's cube number. the original number is always smaller than the cube number. $5 \times 5 \times 5 = 125$ original cube

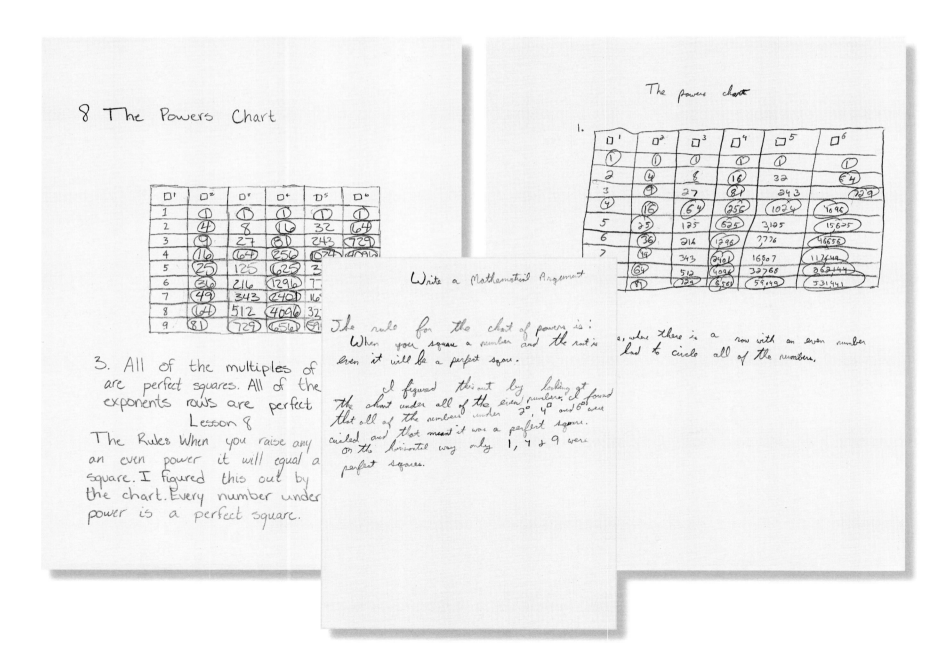

8 The Powers Chart

□¹	□²	□³	□⁴	□⁵	□⁶
1	①	①	①	①	①
2	④	8	⑯	32	㉔
3	⑨	27	⑧⑴	243	⑺⑵⑼
4	⑯	㉔	256	10⒋	⑷⒐⒑
5	㉕	125	㉖㉕	3	
6	㊱	216	⑫⑨⑥	7	
7	㊉	343	㉔⓪⑴	16	
8	㉔	512	④⓪⑨⑥	32	
9	⑧⑴	⑺㉙	㉖⑤⑹	9	

3. All of the multiples of
are perfect squares. All of the
exponents rows are perfect

Lesson 8

The Rule: When you raise any
an even power it will equal a
square. I figured this out by
the chart. Every number under
power is a perfect square.

Write a Mathematical Argument

The rule for the chart of powers is:
When you square a number and the root is
even it will be a perfect square.

I figured this out by looking at
the chart under all of the even numbers. I found
that all of the numbers under 2°, 4° and 6° were
circled and that meant it was a perfect square.
On the horizontal way only 1, 4 & 9 were
perfect squares.

The powers chart

1.

□¹	□²	□³	□⁴	□⁵	□⁶
①	①	①	①	①	①
2	④	8	⑯	32	㉔
3	⑨	27	⑧⑴	243	⑺㉙
④	⑯	㉔	㉖㉕	⑩㉔	⑯⑨⑥
5	㉕	125	㉖㉕	3,125	⑮⑹㉕
6	㊱	216	⑫⑨⑥	7776	④⑥⑥⑤⑥
7	㊉	343	㉔⓪⑴	16807	⑴⑴㉔⑷⑧
㉔	512	④⓪⑨⑥	32768	⑧⑥㉔⑴⑷⑷
⑧⑴	⑺㉙	⑥⑤⑹⑴	59,049	⑤⑶⑴⑷⑷⑴

...s, where there is a row with an even number
...had to circle all of the numbers.

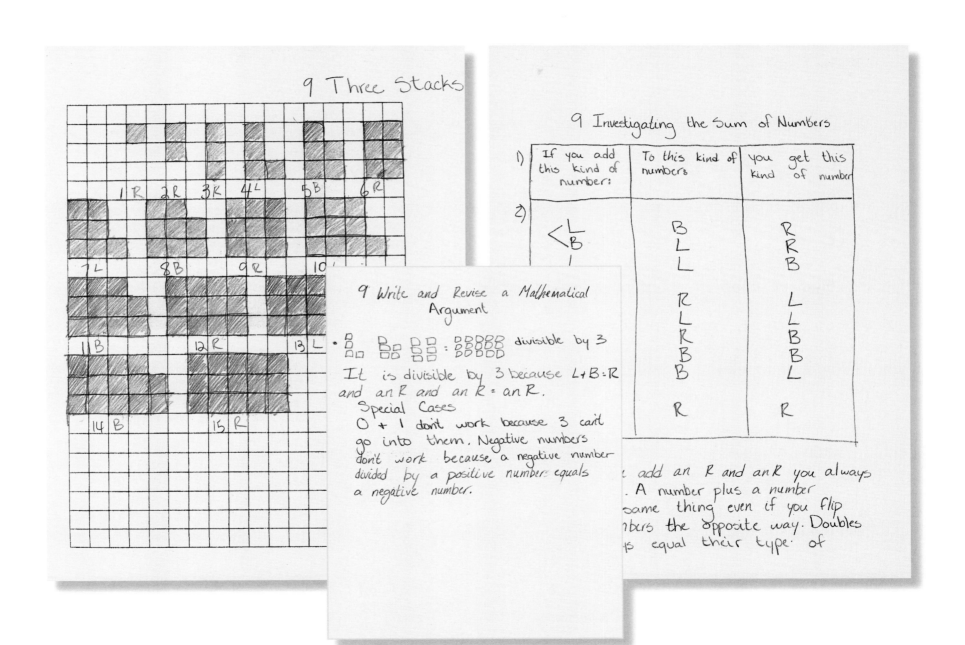

9 Three Stacks

1 R 2 R 3 R 4 L 5 B 6 R
7 L 8 B 9 R 10
11 B 12 R 13 L
14 B 15 R

9 Investigating the Sum of Numbers

If you add this kind of number:	To this kind of numbers	you get this kind of number
< L B 1	B L R L R B B R	R R B L L B L R

...e add an R and an R you always
. A number plus a number
same thing even if you flip
...bers the opposite way. Doubles
...s equal their type of

9 Write and Revise a Mathematical Argument

• □ □□ □□ : □□□□ divisible by 3
  □□ □□ □□   □□□□□

It is divisible by 3 because L+B=R
and an R and an R = an R.
   Special Cases
0 + 1 don't work because 3 can't
go into them. Negative numbers
don't work because a negative number
divided by a positive number equals
a negative number.

Investigate Necessary Machines

1. What necessary machines would you use to get the lengths:

15 - 3+5
28 - 2+2+7
36 - 2+2+3+3
65 - 5+13
84 - 2+2+7+3

2. For the machines in #1, are there any other machine combinatio[ns] have used?
15 - 1, 15
28 - 1, 4, 28
36 - 1, 4, 6, 9, 12, 18, 36

3. What length of bubble gum to go through 5 machine necessary machines? #32, 2,2,2, 2,2

4. What length of bubble gum go through the most n[umber] necessary machines? 6 How figure that out? #64, #96. at the chart.

* "Any number can be written of prime numbers."

Yes I believe so. You can alwa[ys] the number. Let's take 1 and That is why I agree.

Investigate Necessary Machines

1. What machines would you use to get the lengths.

15. 5, 3
28. 7, 2, 2
36. 2, 3, 3, 2
65. 13, 5
84. 2, 2, 7, 3

[...]s in #1, are there any other [com]binations you could have used?
[...], 14, 28 36. 1, 4, 6, 65. 1, 65, 84. 1, 4, 6, 12, 21, 28, 42, 84
9, 12, 18,
36
[...]t bubble gum would need to go [ma]chines, if all 5 were necessary
.2, 2, 2, 2, 2 80. 2, 2, 2, 2, 5
.2, 2, 2, 2, 3
.2, 2, 2, 3, 3
[...] of bubble gum would need to go [...]ost number of necessary
[...]did you figure out your answer?
[...]cause it needs to go through [mach]ine 6 times.
[...]2, 2, 2, 2, 3.

Investigate Necessary Machines

1. What necessary machines would you use to get the lengths:

15 - 5 and 3
28 - 7 and 2 and 2   use #2 twice
36 - 3 and 3 and 2 and 2
     use #3 twice, use #2 twice.
65 - 13 and 5
84 - 3 and 2 and 7 and 2
     use #2 twice

2. For the machines in #1 are there any other machines combinations you could have used?

15 - 1 and 15
28 - 1, 4, 28
36 - 1, 4, 6, 9, 12, 18, 36
65 - 1, 65
84 - 1, 4, 6, 12, 21, 28, 42, 84

3. What length of bubble gum would you need to go through 5 machines, if all 5 were necessary machines?

The length is 32 because you need to use #2 five times just to get 32.

How many times will a Number Appear on a Multiplication Chart?

1x	2x	3x	4x	5x	6x	7x	8x	9x	10x
1	2	4	6	16	12	64	24		
	3	9	8	81	18		66		
	5	25	10		20				
	7	49	14		56				
	11		15						
	13		21						
	17		22						
	19		27						
	23		33						
	41								

Generalize About the Column in Which Any Number Belongs.

If you wanted to predict in which column a number belongs you would need to factor it out. If you factor out a number and it's only factors are one and itself you know it go's in the 2x column because it only has 2 factors. Which also means it's a prime number. So any number when factored out can be put into a [column]. All you need to know is [how m]any factors it has.

Predict in which column a number Belongs!

1.
27 - 4x   1,3,9,27

49 - 3x   1,7,49

33 - 4x   1,11,3,33

66 - 8x   1,2,3,6,11,33,22,66

81 - 5x   1,3,9,27,81

A. All the numbers in the 2x column are prime and only have 2 factors.
B. Any number with 3 factors go's in the 3x column.
C. A number with 6 factors go's in the 6x column.

2.
A. 41
B. 64
C. 56

- Writing a Mathematical Argument

- All the numbers in the 2x column a prime numbers and only have two factors.

- I figured this out by looking at all the numbers in the column, and by looking at the number chart. 2,3,5,7,11,13,17,19,23, and 29 are all prime numbers.

- The rule would work no matter what, because only numbers with two factors can go into the column which are prime numbers. For example: The number 17 only has two factors 17×1, and 1×17 which makes it a prime number.

IT'S VERY WELL EXPLAINED. YOU USED GOOD EXAMPLES.

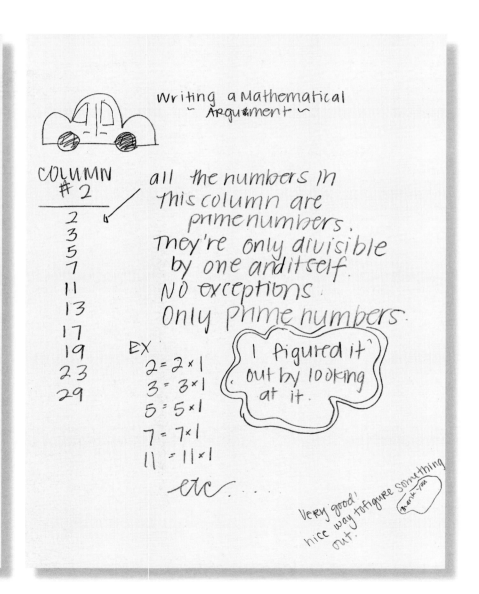

Writing a Mathematical ~ Argument ~

COLUMN #2

2
3
5
7
11
13
17
19
23
29

all the numbers in this column are prime numbers. They're only divisible by one and itself. NO exceptions. Only prime numbers.

EX
2 = 2 × 1
3 = 3 × 1
5 = 5 × 1
7 = 7 × 1
11 = 11 × 1

etc. . . .

I figured it out by looking at it.

Very good! nice way to figure something out. thank you

Assessment Overview

Many opportunities are offered in *Making Mathematical Arguments* to assess students' conceptual understanding and skills related to mathematical arguments about signed number operations, squares, cubes, divisibility, primes, factors, and multiples. This unit contains embedded end-of-phase assessments in Lessons 4, 8, and 12, the last serving as the unit assessment.

To start the unit, have students complete the pre-assessment activity on Teacher's Guide page 6. Use this to assess readiness and growth throughout the unit when compared to students' work in Lesson 9. Also, you will find one skill quiz per phase on Reproducible pages R2–R4. Guidance for optional portfolios is on Assessment pages A18–A19.

The *MathScape* assessment system has been designed to provide flexibility and support for educators in a variety of situations. The core system uses three assessment tools to help you gather information, allowing you to monitor students' individual growth throughout the unit and evaluate their knowledge and abilities at the unit end. Notes from the classroom share teachers' observations about student work, work evaluation, and ways to involve students in the assessment process. Teachers who have adapted this system have found it easy to meet their students' needs.

ASSESSMENT PHILOSOPHY

- Assessment is the shared responsibility of all who are concerned with students' learning in mathematics.
- An assessor can be a teacher, peer, or student.
- Assessment activities focus on what students do know and can do as opposed to what they don't know.
- Assessment activities don't use time as a factor, since speed is almost never relevant to mathematical effectiveness.
- An assessment tool can range from a skill quiz to an embedded, hands-on project.
- It takes a multifaceted assessment system combining traditional tests with performance assessment to create a complete picture of students' learning.

Assessment

C O N T E N T S

ASSESSMENT TOOLS

The three assessment tools—What To Look For, Assessment Rubric, and Skill Check—provide information for fully evaluating your students' learning. The information at the left shows where in the unit you can use each type of tool and on which Assessment page it is described.

What To Look For

The What To Look For questions, which appear on the Teacher's Guide pages, are a short list of what students should be able to do at the end of an investigation. Use the questions as you lead a class discussion, monitor small group activities, or quickly check student work. The Assessment pages for these lessons provide an overview of student work along with teachers' observations.

Skill Check

The Skill Check helps you plan homework in the upcoming phase and review essential skills. It also provides the solutions for the Skill Quiz, a one-page reproducible quiz for each phase that focuses on the specific skills introduced or practiced in that phase. Teachers' notes contain suggestions on ways you can use the assessment information you gather to inform instruction.

Assessment Rubric

The Assessment Rubric describes what student work might look like at four different levels. An Assessment Rubric is provided for each phase assessment and the unit assessment, where it is accompanied by student work and teachers' notes from the classroom. A reproducible of the Assessment Criteria, corresponding to level 3 of the Assessment Rubric, is also available for student use. A general assessment rubric is provided for evaluating portfolios, which are an optional part of the assessment system.

Reporting to Parents

Although not in itself an assessment tool, the Reporting to Parents page brings together the rich information gathered by the What To Look For, Assessment Rubric, and Skill Check tools, and provides guidance in assigning letter grades. If you need to assign one grade for the entire unit, the information gathered from the different assessment tools can be recorded on the Assessment Checklist, page A3, to help you maintain a balance between concepts, skills, and processes.

ASSESSMENT CHECKLIST

The Assessment Checklist is on Reproducible page R1. You can use it to record the information gathered about each student with the different assessment tools and to note your observations. You can also give students their own copies of the checklist that they can use to organize and reflect on their work for their portfolios.

I used a completed Assessment Checklist for each student to let parents know what their child had accomplished during the unit, what skills they had learned, scores on assignments, and what was seen as still needing work in terms of skills and concepts. I attached it to their portfolio and sent it home at progress report time. The blank Assessment Checklist served as a beginning-of-the-year informational piece for parents at back-to-school nights. It allowed parents to see first hand and early in the year what topics and skills would be covered. □

The Assessment Checklist is useful for my students who are absent. They can refer to the checklist for the lessons they missed and make sure that they pick up the assignments that they need. This does not necessarily require that every student have a checklist. I have a main list on the board with assignment dates and so on. □

Making Mathematical Arguments
ASSESSMENT CHECKLIST

Period: ___ Date: ___

Name: Lesson	Assignment Description	Assessment	Notes
Pre-assessment	What is involved in writing a mathematical argument?	OK	no counterexamples in writing
Lesson 1	Statements About Signs	—	some confusion about signed number operations
Lesson 2	Counterexamples and Cube Combinations	✛	
Lesson 3	More Cases to Consider	✛	
Lesson 4	Rules to Operate By	3✛	better understanding of signed number operations
Phase One Skill Check	Skill Quiz 1 & Homework 1–4	90%	
Lesson 5	Perfect Pattern Predictions	✛	
Lesson 6	Counterexamples and Special Cases	✛	needs work with cube roots
Lesson 7	Root Relationships	—	
Lesson 8	A Powerful Argument	3	
Phase Two Skill Check	Skill Quiz 2 & Homework 5–8	85%	
Lesson 9	Three-Stack Shape Sums	✛	
Lesson 10	A Stretching Problem	✛	
Lesson 11	Pattern Appearances	✛	
Lesson 12	The Final Arguments	3✛	good grasp of factors and primes
Phase Three Skill Check	Skill Quiz 3 & Homework 9–12	95%	
Post-assessment	What is involved in writing a mathematical argument?	OK	used counterexamples effectively

Comments: Has shown much growth in understanding of exponents and radicals. Is willing to ask questions when concepts are not understood. The final mathematical argument written from scratch was well thought out and showed much effort.

Assessment

When students had written all the factor pairs of a number in order, they saw that the pairs began to repeat once all the unique factors had been listed. The factor pair with the least difference between the two factors (4 and 4) had the last pair of unique factors. The dimensions of the rectangles also began to reverse when all the possibilities had been made. The square or the rectangle closest to being a square was the last one with unique dimensions. One student pointed out that a square is really a rectangle with four equal sides. □

Pre-assessment

You can use the Pre-assessment on page 6 of the Teacher's Guide to assess the prerequisites for the unit. At the end of the unit, you can compare this task to Lesson 9 to note growth that has occurred in the course of the unit. (See Post-assessment, page A17.)

DO STUDENTS' PRE-ASSESSMENTS DEMONSTRATE THE PREREQUISITES OF:

- familiarity with operations involving fractions and decimals?

- understanding of what numbers are included in whole numbers and signed numbers?

- ability to interpret numbers expressed in exponential form as powers of a number?

- experience in identifying and describing patterns?

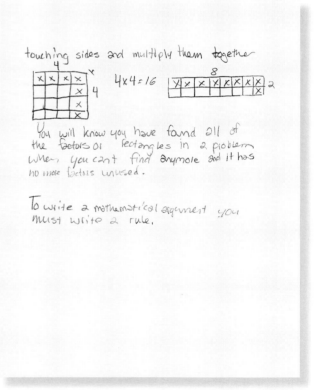

Phase One: Lessons 1, 2 & 3

The student work from Lessons 1, 2, and 3 of this phase should show an increased understanding of signed number operations and counterexamples. One common error to look for in students' work is that they may confuse the sign of the answer that results when multiplying or dividing with negative numbers, especially when multiplying or dividing a negative number by a negative number.

Some students thought that negative − negative would always be negative because "you are always negative." So as a class we went over lots of examples that showed that negative − negative could be negative, positive, or zero. Using the number line was helpful for several students. Another misconception my students had was that a positive × negative (or positive ÷ negative) could be positive or negative. We reviewed as a class that for example 2 × (−3) means 2 groups of negative 3 and used cubes to model problems like this. □

1. The statement that says that a positive plus a negative is always a negative because −4+6=2 is a counterexample.
2. The statement that says that a negative number minus a positive number will always be negative is true because we could find no counterexample.
3. The statement that says any time you start with a positive number and subtract a negative number, you will have to add zero pairs is true because we could find no counterexample.
4. The statement that says that a negative number minus a negative number is a negative number is not true because of the counterexample −6−−7=1.
5. The statement that says that a negative decimal number added to a positive decimal number is zero is false because of the counterexample −.50 + .75 = .25.
6. The statement that says that a positive fraction minus a negative fraction will always get you more than 1 is false because of the counterexample ¼ −−½ = ¾.
7. The statement that says that a negative decimal plus a negative decimal has a negative answer is true because we could find no counterexample.
8. The statement that says th[...] you have to add zero pa[...] the counterexample −3−−2=[...]
9. The statement that says th[...] zero-pairs when adding is t[...] no counterexample.

Sort the solutions

1. ✓ positive + positive = positive
   ✗ positive + negative = positive or negative
   ✗ positive + positive = positive or negative
   ✗ negative + negative = negative
   ✓ negative + negative = positive or negative
   ✗ positive − positive = positive
   ✓ positive − negative = negative
   ✓ negative − positive = negative
   ✓ negative − negative = negative

2. The ones with the ✓ can always be predicted. The ones with the ✗ depend on the numbers in the equation.

   5−4=1
   5−6=−1

Create Statements and Counter Examples
1. a positive plus another positive will equal a negative.
2. a positive minus a negative equals a negative.
3. a negative multiplyed by a P equals a p.
4. a N divided by a P equals a P.
5. a P plus a P equals positive.
6. a N subtract a N equals negative.
7. a P times a N can be P or N.
8. a P ÷ a N can be P or N.

Assessment

It's important that students' responses show an understanding of equivalencies and the counterexamples demonstrate that they fit the statement for which they were intended. It should also be evident that the student could state the rule for multiplying and dividing several signed numbers together. I gave the work a level 3 if all of the criteria was met but sophistication and detail were not evident. ☐

I gave work a level 3 if the responses were short, but complete and accurate and the student's explanation of equivalencies as well as multiplying and dividing several signed numbers was clear and concise. ☐

Although one student had listed the correct results of the combinations for Is it Always True?, there were no counterexamples to show whether or not the student knew what they were or how to find them. The work showed that the student did not have an understanding of the rule for multiplying and dividing several signed numbers together. In this case, I gave the work a level 2. ☐

4 3 2 1 Phase One: Lesson 4

For the embedded assessment in Lesson 4, Rules to Operate By, students applied what they had learned in Phase One to find equivalent operations and determine if mathematical statements are true. The Assessment Rubric on the opposite page is designed to help you evaluate student work. See Reproducible page R5 for a version of the level 3 assessment criteria worded for student use.

Is it Always True?
- Positive + Positive = Positive. Always true because if you add a positive you are going up on the number line.
- Positive + Negative = Negative 8+2=6
- Negative + Negative = Negative Always true because you are making it more negative by adding ne
- Positive - Positive = Positive 3-5=-
- Positive - Negative = Positive. Always is like adding a positive.
- Negative - Positive = Negative. Always is like adding a negative.
- Negative - Negative = Negative -2-

1. a. negative 1
   b. positive 2
   c. negative 3
   d. positive 4
2. When you multiply several numb positive if there are on even will be negative if there are on
3. No counterexample
4. The statement is the same as divide instead of multiply in #2.

Is it Always True?
P+P=P ✓ It is always true because it's adding more
P+N=N false 5+1=4
N+N=N It's always true because it's like adding more negatives
P-P=P false 3-4=-1
    like adding positive
    ; like adding negatives

Determine Whether a Statement is Always True

1.
    a. negative   c. negative
    b. positive   d. positive

2. If you multiplied a positive times a negative, you get a negative. If you multiplied a negative x's a negative, you get a positive. Positive x's a positive you get a positive.

3. There are no need for counterexamples.

4. ¿?
    Positive + Positive = Positive
    Positive + Negative = Positive, Negative, or Zero
    Negative + Negative = Negative
    Positive - Positive = Positive, Negative, Zero
    Positive - Negative = Positive
    Negative - Negative = Positive, Negative, Zero
    Negative - Positive = Negative

3
4

e numbers is even, the answer is positive.
e numbers is odd, the answer is negative.

multiplication, even when division is involved.

Does student work...

- show a sophisticated under-standing of equivalencies—that subtracting a negative is equiv-alent to adding a positive, and that subtracting a positive is equivalent to adding a negative?

- show in detail how to find appropriate counterexamples?

- describe clearly and accurately the rule for multiplying and dividing several signed num-bers together?

- show a very clear understand-ing that for a mathematical statement to be a rule it must be always true?

Goes beyond expectations

- show an understanding of equivalencies—that subtracting a negative is equivalent to adding a positive, and that sub-tracting a positive is equivalent to adding a negative?

- show how to find appropriate counterexamples?

- describe the rule for multiply-ing and dividing several signed numbers together?

- show an understanding that for a mathematical statement to be a rule it must be always true?

Meets all expectations

- show some understanding of equivalencies—that subtracting a negative is equivalent to adding a positive, and that sub-tracting a positive is equivalent to adding a negative?

- show counterexamples with some errors?

- describe the rule for multiply-ing and dividing several signed numbers together with some errors?

- show some understanding that for a mathematical statement to be a rule it must be always true?

Meets some expectations

- show a lack of understanding that subtracting a negative is equivalent to adding a positive, and that subtracting a positive is equivalent to adding a negative?

- show either no counterexam-ples or a few that are incorrect?

- describe a rule for multiplying and dividing several signed numbers together that is either inaccurate or incomplete?

- show little or no understanding that for a mathematical state-ment to be a rule it must be always true?

Falls below expectations

Assessment

I was really impressed with the growth I saw in my students in terms of signed numbers. The cubes helped many students better understand signed number operations. I felt that the homework problems were worthwhile and helped to prepare students further for the quiz in this phase. □

SKILL CHECK

Phase One: Homework & Quiz

Students' conceptual understanding in Phase One is monitored daily using the **What To Look For** and evaluated using the **Assessment Rubric.** The lesson homework and the **Phase One Skill Quiz** are tools to check skill proficiency.

Homework

Homework for Lessons 1–4 appears in the Student Guide on pages 34–37. Answers for this homework are on Assessment pages A29–A32. Depending on the needs of your students, you may assign all or part of the homework for each lesson. You may want to take students' homework performance into consideration as part of the overall phase evaluation.

Skill Quiz

The Phase One Skill Quiz is provided on Reproducible page R2. Solutions are given here. Hot Topics for Phase One are:

- Counterexamples
- Addition and Subtraction of Fractions
- Integer Operations
- Statistics

SKILL QUIZ ANSWERS

1. -2 2. 0 3. 3
4. -7; Check students' drawings.
5. -3; Check students' drawings.
6. 6; Check students' drawings.
7. -7 Check students' drawings.
8. -5 9. -9 10. 1
11. -30 12. 3 13. -10
14. -8 15. -28 16. -12
17. $2 + (-6)$ 18. $3 + 2$ 19. $-7 + 11$
20. 5 positive cubes; 3 positive, 2 negative cubes; 2 positive cubes, 3 negative cubes; 1 positive cube, 4 negative cubes; 5 negative cubes; problems will vary.
21. Not always true; if you add a negative number and a positive number, the answer will sometimes be negative.
22. always true
23. Not always true; if you add a negative fraction to a negative fraction, the answer will sometimes be smaller than $-\frac{1}{8}$.
24. Answers will vary. Positive + Negative, Positive − Positive, and Negative − Negative could have counterexamples.

Phase Two: Lessons 5, 6 & 7

The student work from Lessons 5, 6, and 7 of this phase should show an increased understanding of what a mathematical argument is and how to write one. One common error to look for in students' work is failure to check for all the special cases in a mathematical argument.

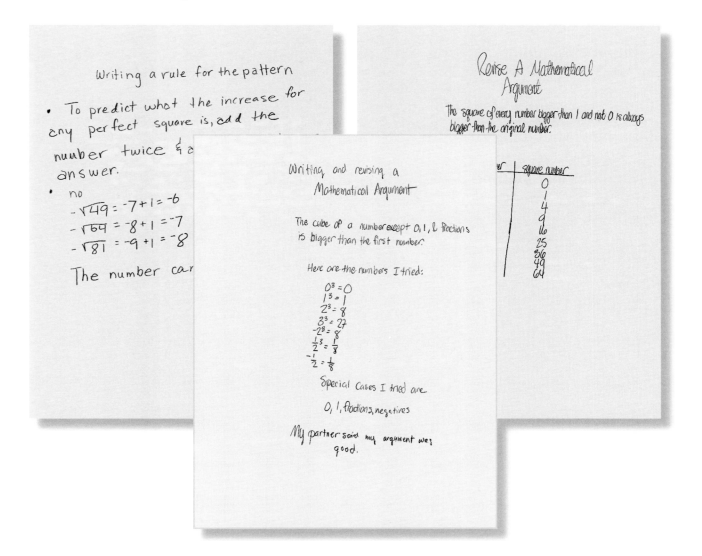

Writing a rule for the pattern

• To predict what the increase for any perfect square is, add the number twice & a ... answer.

• no
$-\sqrt{49} = -7 + 1 = -6$
$-\sqrt{64} = -8 + 1 = -7$
$-\sqrt{81} = -9 + 1 = -8$

The number car ...

Revise A Mathematical Argument

The square of every number bigger than 1 and not 0 is always bigger than the original number.

er	square number
	0
	1
	4
	9
	16
	25
	36
	49
	64

Writing and revising a Mathematical Argument

The cube of a number except 0, 1, & fractions is bigger than the first number.

Here are the numbers I tried:
$0^3 = 0$
$1^3 = 1$
$2^3 = 8$
$3^3 = 27$
$-2^3 = 8$
$\frac{1}{2}^3 = \frac{1}{8}$
$-\frac{1}{2} = \frac{1}{8}$

Special Cases I tried are
0, 1, fractions, negatives

My partner said my argument was good.

I would emphasize next time that those students who were reviewing their partner's mathematical arguments look very carefully at the arguments. Some of my students overlooked errors in, for example, the rule that a negative number cubed is always a negative number. I would encourage the students who are providing feedback to go through each one of the counterexamples to verify that they are correct. I would also make sure that students check all of the specials cases when writing their arguments. □

Marino clearly and correctly stated a rule about the patterns of perfect squares and used the chart as a method of figuring out the rule. Counterexamples and special cases were included but not explained. However, he did revise the rule to incorporate the special cases. I gave this work a 3. □

One of my students only tested the rule using positive integers and did not test any special cases or find any counterexamples. The student thought about the rule only as stated and did not investigate it any further. The student showed no evidence of revising the rule. I gave this work a level 2. □

I also gave work a 2 if the student did not seem to understand the rule as stated or if the student did not know what a perfect square was and failed to revise the rule. □

In Lesson 8, A Powerful Argument, students applied what they had learned in Phase Two to write a mathematical argument about squares, roots, or exponents based on a pattern they found in the Powers Chart. The Assessment Rubric on the opposite page is designed to help you evaluate student work. See Reproducible page R5 for a version of the level 3 assessment criteria worded for student use.

"IF YOU RAISE ANY NUMBER TO AN EVEN POWER, THE RESULT WILL BE A PERFECT SQUARE."

I AGREE BECAUSE ON THE CHART WE DID EARLIER IT PROVED THIS POINT. YET THERE ARE SOME EXCEPTIONS LIKE O AND FRACTIONS.

REVISED
IF YOU RAISE ANY NUMBER EXCEPT O AND FRACTIONS TO AN EVEN POWER, THE RESULT WILL BE A PERFECT SQUARE.

If you raise any number to an even power, the result will be a perfect square. (2,4,6,8,10,12) The result would be a perfect square. Well I agree, because it is true because when you raise an even power then the result comes out even. Like for example: $4^4 = 256 = 16 = 4$ So that is why I think that any answer is correct, because due to the fact as we know four is a even number. So that is why I agree.

"If you raise any number to an even power, the result will be a perfect square".

I disagree because it will not be a perfect square when you have an odd number, even though you have an even power. Ex: $9^4 = 6561 = 81$

Does student work...

- show a sophisticated understanding of patterns of perfect squares involving powers of numbers arranged on a grid?

- clearly and correctly state a rule about the patterns of perfect squares in rows or columns of the grid?

- describe methods used to figure out the rule and include counterexamples that are detailed and show much effort?

- include a clear and detailed explanation of all special cases for which the rule does not work?

- show a basic understanding of patterns of perfect squares involving powers of numbers arranged on a grid?

- clearly state a rule about the patterns of perfect squares in rows or columns of the grid that is mostly correct?

- describe methods used to figure out the rule and include counterexamples?

- include an explanation of special cases for which the rule does not work?

- show a somewhat limited understanding of patterns of perfect squares involving powers of numbers arranged on a grid?

- state a rule about the patterns of perfect squares in rows or columns of the grid with some errors?

- describe methods used to figure out the rule and include counterexamples with some errors?

- include a limited explanation of some of the special cases for which the rule does not work?

- show little understanding of patterns of perfect squares involving powers of numbers arranged on a grid?

- state a rule about the patterns of perfect squares in rows or columns of the grid that is either incomplete or incorrect?

- describe methods used to figure out the rule and include counterexamples that are either incomplete or mostly incorrect?

- include little or no explanation of the special cases for which the rule does not work?

 **Goes beyond expectations**

 Meets all expectations

 Meets some expectations

 Falls below expectations

SKILL CHECK

Phase Two: Homework & Quiz

Students' conceptual understanding in **Phase Two** is monitored daily using the **What To Look For** and evaluated using the **Assessment Rubric. The lesson homework and the Phase Two Skill Quiz are tools to check skill proficiency.**

Homework

Homework for Lesson 5–8 appears in the Student Guide on pages 38–41. Answers for this homework are on Assessment pages A33–A36. Depending on the needs of your students, you may assign all or part of the homework for each lesson. You may want to take students' homework performance into consideration as part of the overall phase evaluation.

Skill Quiz

The Phase Two Skill Quiz is provided on Reproducible page R3. Solutions are given here. Hot Topics for Phase Two are:

- Powers and Exponents
- Square and Cube Roots
- Counterexamples
- Length and Distance

SKILL QUIZ ANSWERS

1. 169   2. 841   3. 11   4. 26

5. 125   6. −2,744   7. 8   8. −12

9. 2,401   10. 2,187   11. 15   12. 31

13. 3rd and 4th   14. 12th and 13th

15. 66th and 67th   16. 130th and 131st

17. Smaller; Explanations will vary.

18–20. Larger; Explanations will vary.

21. Estimates will vary. Actual square roots to two decimal places are:

   a. 4.47   b. 13.96   c. 27.02

22. Answers will vary.   23. no; no; no; no; yes

24. For 0 and 1 the cube root and square root are equal. For negative numbers, it is not possible to take the square root. For proper fractions, the cube root is larger than the square root.

25. The cube root of any number greater than 1 is smaller than the square root of the same number.

26–28. No; Explanations will vary.

29. Yes; 4 is a perfect square.

30. Yes; The exponent is even.

31. Yes; 9 is a perfect square.

32. No; Yes, exponent is divisible by 3; Yes, 8 is a perfect cube; no; Yes, the exponent is divisible by 3; Yes, the exponent is divisible by 3.

33. 243; 1,953,125; 32,768; 16,384; 1,771,561; 387,420,489

34. See answers to items 26–31.

Phase Three: Lessons 9, 10 & 11

The student work from Lessons 9, 10, and 11 of this phase should show an increased understanding of making generalizations in their mathematical arguments about why they know a rule is true. One common error to look for in students' work is a failure to articulate clearly why a rule is true rather than just giving examples.

It was a real challenge to motivate some of the students to look for counterexamples and consider special cases. They often accepted the rule given as the way it was supposed to be mathematically. I had these students pair up with students who were discussing and creating counterexamples and going through the special cases. This seemed to motivate those students who were having difficulty so that they were able to begin to go through this process on their own. □

Write a Mathematical Argument:

"Whenever you add 3 consecutive whole numbers together, the sum will be divisible by 3."

If you add 3 consecutive numbers together. Divide it by 3 and the answer will be the number in the middle. Example: 3+4+5 = 3+4+5 = 12 3)12 4

This is true because when you divide 3 by 12, the answer will be 4. 4 is the number in the middle.

When you add 3 con[...]
It is like adding L,R
□ 目 目 = R   w[...]

目 目 ← Rectangles "3"[...]

"Any number can be written as the product of prime factors."

No, because you can't use zero, and decimals and fractions. You can't get a machine with decimals because all the machines are whole numbers.

Revised
"Any number > 1 that is positive can be written as the product of prime factors."

Generalize About the Column in Which Any Number Belongs
I could predict where a # belongs because I saw and noticed a pattern. The 1x column would only have 1 # in it which is one. It is there because it only has one factor. In the 2x column they are all prime #s. In column 3x the #s there only have 3 factors like 49, 4, and 25. I know in the 4x column the #s there only have 4 factors. For example, #s like 6, 8, 10, and 14. So in each column, depending on the #s, only has #s with a certain factor like in the 6x column, there would be #s with 6 factors like 12, 18, and 20. That's why I can predict where a # belongs to.

I gave Shanti a level 3 because she had stated a rule about patterns in the Multiplication Chart that was correct for the most part even though she did not include that the numbers in the 3-times column are perfect squares of prime numbers. The revision showed that she did add more mathematical support through examples as suggested by the partner. I would have liked to have seen more evidence that she had considered special cases. □

I gave one student a 3 because the rule the student stated showed that thought had been given to the way the rule was worded. The student noted that the rule works in all cases, even though the work did not show what cases were considered. The work showed that the student understood the meaning of prime numbers. □

In Lesson 12, The Final Arguments, students applied what they had learned in the unit to a final project, develop their own mathematical argument from scratch. The Assessment Rubric on the opposite page is designed to help you evaluate student work. See Reproducible page R6 for a version of the level 3 assessment criteria worded for student use.

Writing a Mathematical Argument

1. Numbers that appear in the "3x" column can only be factored by 3 numbers and are generally squared numbers.
2. I figured this out by going through a multiplication chart from 1 to 100 and looked for numbers that only appear three times.
3. As I said, numbers in the "3x" column are squared like 25 and 49. Although, some squared numbers like 36 and 16 wouldn't go in this column because it can't be factored only 3 times.

It's fine. It would be better if you use some mathematical support. Other than that it is a great

Writing a Mathematical Argument

1. Numbers that appear in the "3x" column can only be factored by 3 numbers and are generally squared numbers.
2. I figured this out by going through a multiplication chart from 1 to 100 and looked for numbers that only appear 3 times.
3. As I said, numbers in the "3x" column are squared like 25 (5^2) and 49 (7^2). Although, some squared numbers like 36 (6^2) and 16 (4^2) wouldn't go in this column because it can't be factored only 3 times.
Ex:

25 - 1:5, 5:1, 5:5 goes in "3x" column
36 - 1:36, 36:1, 6:6, 4:9, 9:4, 3:12, 12:3
"3x" column.

Writing a Mathematical Argument

My rule is that all the numbers for the 2x column are all prime numbers. I figured this out by making a chart that shows how many times a number will appear on the multiplication chart. I also figured this out when I looked at the 2x column, I realized that all the numbers can only be divided by itself and 1. It works in all cases, only if the numbers are prime numbers.

This is very clearly written!

Does student work...

- show a sophisticated mathematical understanding of factors, primes, squares, and cubes?

- show that much thought and effort were given to choosing a mathematical argument?

- clearly state a rule about patterns in the Multiplication Chart that is precise and correct?

- accurately and clearly describe methods used to figure out the rule and include appropriate counterexamples?

- include a detailed and comprehensive explanation of all the special cases for which the rule does not work?

- show a general mathematical understanding of factors, primes, squares, and cubes?

- show that thought was given to choosing a mathematical argument?

- state a rule about patterns in the Multiplication Chart that is mostly correct?

- describe methods used to figure out the rule and include appropriate counterexamples?

- include an explanation of the special cases for which the rule does not work?

- show some mathematical understanding of factors, primes, squares, and cubes?

- show that some thought was given to choosing a mathematical argument?

- state a somewhat erroneous rule about patterns in the Multiplication Chart?

- partially describe methods used to figure out the rule and include counterexamples that are not clear or have some errors?

- include only a brief explanation of some of the special cases for which the rule does not work?

- show little mathematical understanding of factors, primes, squares, and cubes?

- show that little thought was given to choosing a mathematical argument?

- state a rule about patterns in the Multiplication Chart that either is incomplete or has major errors?

- fail to describe methods used to figure out the rule or include counterexamples that have major errors?

- include little or no explanation of the special cases for which the rule does not work?

 Goes beyond expectations

 Meets all expectations

 Meets some expectations

 Falls below expectations

Assessment

Many of my students were very enthusiastic about the divisibility homework in Lesson 9 because they loved drawing the L, b, and rectangle numbers. When they completed the homework problems about a 4-stack model, I could tell that they had applied what they had learned about the 3-stack model to the 4-stack model. In Lesson 11, several students expanded the Multiplication Chart through 20 rows and 20 columns on their own time at home so that they could accurately verify their answers. □

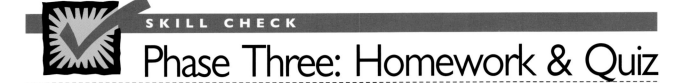

SKILL CHECK
Phase Three: Homework & Quiz

Students' conceptual understanding in Phase Three is monitored daily using the **What To Look For** and evaluated using the **Assessment Rubric.** The lesson homework and the **Phase Three Skill Quiz** are tools to check skill proficiency.

Homework

Homework for Lessons 9–12 appears in the Student Guide on pages 42–45. Answers for this homework are on Assessment pages A37–A40. Depending on the needs of your students, you may assign all or part of the homework for each lesson. You may want to take students' homework performance into consideration as part of the overall phase evaluation.

Skill Quiz

The Phase Three Skill Quiz is provided on Reproducible page R4. Solutions are given here. Hot Topics for Phase Three are:

- Factors and Multiples
- Counterexamples
- Powers and Exponents
- Perimeter
- Statistics

SKILL QUIZ ANSWERS

1. rectangle number
2. L number
3. b number

4. rectangle number, b number
5. rectangle number
6. b number
7. necessary
8. unnecessary
9. necessary
10. unnecessary
11. necessary
12. necessary
13. 3, 3, 3
14. 2, 19
15. 2, 2, 13
16. 2, 2, 3, 7
17. 64 in.: 2, 2, 2, 2, 2, 2; 96 in.: 2, 2, 2, 2, 2, 3

18.

1 time	2×	3×	4×	5×	6×	7×	8×	9×	10×
1	2	4	6	16	12		24		
	3	9	8		18				
	5	25	10		20				
	7		14						
	11		15						
	13		21						
	17		22						
	19								
	23								

19. 2×   20. 3×   21. 6×   22. 2×   23. 6×

24. Answers will vary.

25. Columns 2× and 4× (15 numbers each)

26. They are squares of prime numbers; they are prime numbers.

27. In the 4× column. The cube of a prime number has four factors: 1, the prime number, the square of the prime number, and the cube of the prime number.

Post-assessment

To get a sense of your students' growth over the course of the unit, you can compare students' pre-assessment work (see page A4) with their work from Lesson 9. Ask students to write a second response to the question: What is involved in writing a mathematical argument? Compare this to their pre-assessment writing.

DID STUDENTS DEMONSTRATE GROWTH IN:

- gaining familiarity with using models to find factors of numbers?

- writing a rule about a mathematical concept?

- finding counterexamples if necessary?

- describing methods used to figure out the rule?

- describing and explaining all of the special cases for which the rule does not work?

Most of my students showed growth in understanding what a mathematical argument was and the steps involved in writing one. Before we began this unit, my students had never heard of a counterexample and testing for special cases. By the end of the unit, you could hear comments such as, "I found one counterexample so that proves it's not true." Although students usually tested for the four special cases suggested in the unit (0, 1, fractions, and negative numbers), I felt that they still needed more experience with generalizing rules to cover all cases. But for now, they had been exposed to the possibilities, so they were off to a good start □

> To write a mathematical argument you must write a statement first and see if it is always true.
>
> You look for counterexamples to try to find things that make the statement false.
>
> You test for special cases like 0, 1, fractions and negative numbers.
>
> Then you revise the statement to make it into a rule that is always true and general.

> touching sides and multiply them together
>
> 4×4=16
>
> You will know you have found all of the factors or rectangles in a problem when you can't find anymore and it has no more factors unused.
>
> To write a mathematical argument you must write a rule.

Assessment

Portfolio Review

One way to assemble portfolios is to give the students at the beginning of the quarter a handout that lists the kinds of work that the teacher will want to see at the end of the quarter. This allows students to be thinking all quarter about what work they will need to save, and will eliminate the need for them to save all of their work. The teacher may also want to have the students include a write-up that talks about what they learned overall during the quarter, what they think they deserve in terms of a grade, and what their goals are for next quarter. Some of the items I asked for were:

* *a problem-solving paper*
* *a paper showing the student's best work*
* *a paper where the student did not do well (including an explanation about what went wrong and how they could improve it)*
* *an ending project*
* *a written explanation of how to do something from the unit*
* *a "show me" paper that shows that the student has mastered some skill* ☐

The focus of the portfolio evaluation is to gain insight into students' growth over time and to see how they view themselves as mathematicians. The portfolio should show students' increasing ability to communicate mathematically, solve problems, and make mathematical connections. The Assessment Rubric on the opposite page is designed to help you evaluate student work.

FOR THIS UNIT THE FOLLOWING ITEMS WORK ESPECIALLY WELL TO SUPPLEMENT A STUDENT'S BASIC PORTFOLIO:

* a photo or sketch of the student's work with manipulatives or a photo of a large project that will not fit in the portfolio
* a table of contents
* a student's original problem, including the solution

Does the portfolio show...

- significant mathematical growth in the understanding and application of unit goals?
- significant mathematical growth in skill development?
- creativity and quality of work that go beyond the requirements of the assignments?
- timely completion of assignments?
- no significant mathematical errors in assigned work?
- clear, coherent, and thoughtful explanations of the mathematical process?

Goes beyond expectations

- some mathematical growth in the understanding and application of unit goals?
- some mathematical growth in skill development?
- acceptable quality of work?
- timely completion of assignments?
- no significant mathematical errors in assigned work?
- clear explanations of the mathematical process?

Meets all expectations

- an understanding and application of unit goals?
- skill development documented with little growth?
- inconsistent quality of work?
- assignments are complete but not always on time?
- minor mathematical errors in the assigned work?
- unclear explanations of the mathematical process?

Meets some expectations

- that key points in the understanding and application of unit goals were missed?
- that skill development is not documented?
- that the quality of work is consistently poor?
- that assignments are consistently late?
- significant mathematical errors in assigned work?
- no explanations of the mathematical process?

Falls below expectations

Assessment

I used the final project rubric as 50% of the unit grade and combined the phase assessments, homework, and daily work as another 25%. The remaining 25% was split between their grades on the skill quizzes, some traditional tests I gave, and their class participation (problem solving and cooperative group work). I explained to parents that the final projects represented concepts, skills, and problem solving. □

I sometimes grade the pieces of a portfolio as well as the write-up descriptions of the pieces at one time; however, if the student has put already graded work into the portfolio, I grade only the write-up descriptions and whether the portfolio is complete. If the portfolio contains items that are revisions, then I regrade only those pieces in the portfolio. □

Reporting to Parents

If you need to assign a single letter grade to reflect all the rich information students have gathered over the course of the unit, remember to maintain a balance between concepts, skills, and processes when doing so.

Skill Proficiency

By combining the Skill Checks, Homework, and any Handbook assignments, you should be able to demonstrate to parents their child's ability to practice the skills involving signed number operations that involve exponents beyond the contexts of the in-class investigations. Although skills in signed number operations and exponents are an integral part of the daily lessons in this unit, Lesson 7, Root Relationships, in which students consider positive and negative cube roots as well as square roots, is an obvious example to show parents how skills are incorporated into an investigation.

Conceptual Understanding

In this unit, the concepts covered in the embedded phase assessments for Phases One and Two are also incorporated into the mathematical argument each student develops from scratch at the end of Phase Three. As a result, parents can see their child's conceptual understanding of how to find counterexamples from Phase One, combined with the testing of special cases in a mathematical argument in Phase Two, demonstrated in the final mathematical argument the student produces in Lesson 12, The Final Arguments. You

can also use Lesson 9, Three-Stack Shape Sums, as a specific example to demonstrate to parents how an investigation introduces number theory that is an essential foundation for the study of algebra in high school.

Mathematical Processes

Logical reasoning and mathematical communication occur regularly in daily lessons. The final mathematical argument is ideal for showing parents the nature of the logical reasoning and mathematical communication processes in which their child is engaged. The pattern seeking for the final mathematical argument and communicating about the mathematical argument in written and oral group discussions are rich, real-world experiences for the student. You may want to invite parents to visit the class for a presentation of the students' completed final arguments.

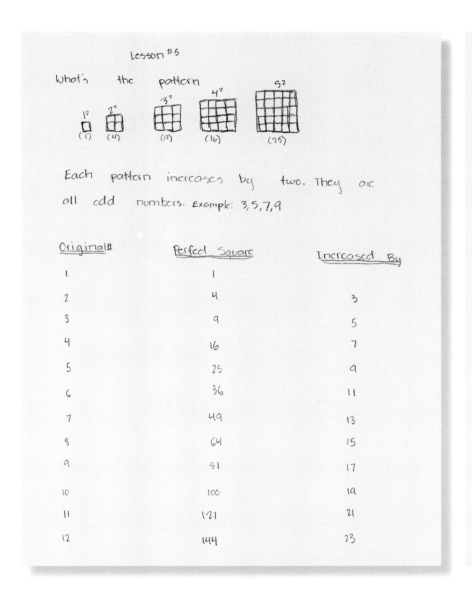

Lesson #5

What's the pattern

1^2 2^2 3^2 4^2 5^2
(1) (4) (9) (16) (25)

Each pattern increases by two. They are all odd numbers. Example: 3,5,7,9

Original #	Perfect Square	Increased By
1	1	
2	4	3
3	9	5
4	16	7
5	25	9
6	36	11
7	49	13
8	64	15
9	81	17
10	100	19
11	121	21
12	144	23
13	169	25
14	196	27
15	225	29
16	256	31
17	289	33
18	324	35
19	361	37
20	400	39
21	441	41
22	484	43
23	529	45
24	576	47
25	625	49
26	676	51
27	729	53
28	784	55
29	841	57
30	900	59
31	961	61
32	1024	63
33		

MAKING MATHEMATICAL ARGUMENTS

Paper 1 (left):

Finding a method to Predict the increase

$$5 - 4 = 2$$
$$7 - 9 = 3$$
$$9 - 16 = 4$$
$$11 - 25 = 5$$
$$13 - 36 = 6$$

One of the ways

Out is to multiply the number

one.

$$529 \times 2 = 1058 + 1 = 1059$$
$$1089 \times 2 = 2178 + 1 = 217$$
$$2401 \times 2 = 4802 + 1 = 480$$

Paper 2 (right):

Finding a method to Predict the increase

$$2 \rightarrow 4 = 5$$
$$3 \rightarrow 9 = 7$$
$$4 \rightarrow 16 = 9$$
$$5 \rightarrow 25 = 11$$
$$6 \rightarrow 36 = 13$$

$$44 \rightarrow 44 + 44 + 1 = 89$$

I add the number twice then add one more.

$$529 \rightarrow 1059$$
$$1089 \rightarrow 2179$$
$$2401 \rightarrow 4803$$

$$+33 + 1 = 67$$

Paper 3 (center):

Finding a Method to predict the increase

$$44 \rightarrow 44 + 44 + 1 = 89$$
$$63 \rightarrow 63 + 63 + 1 = 127$$

$$529 \rightarrow 529 + 529 + 1 = 1059$$
$$1089 \rightarrow 1089 + 1089 + 1 = 2179$$
$$2401 \rightarrow 2401 + 2401 + 1 = 4803$$

The way I got the answers was I added the number twice & added one and I got My answer.

Lesson #6

Special Cases

#1) In Dan's rule it depends because ex: $-1^2 = 1$ Well actually I think that he is correct because ex: $-3^2 (-3)(-3) = 9$. So yes, the number does get bigger cause you $\times$ it by itself, and how many times the little number it is supposed to be $\times$ by, in order to get your answer.

#2) Can you find any counter examples: No I can't find any counter examples like $-1^n = 1$ or just the opposite. Actually yes, you can because ex: $\frac{1}{9} \times \frac{1}{9} = \frac{1}{81}$ So $\frac{1}{9}$ is bigger than $\frac{1}{81}$. Another Ex: $\frac{1}{4} \times \frac{1}{4} = \frac{1}{16}$ the bigger one is $\frac{1}{4}$ cause it is $\frac{1}{16}$ Ex.

So $\frac{1}{4}$ is bigger than $\frac{1}{16}$

#3) Dan's rule can work only with some number greater than one. But like in some other ways Dan's rule is also wrong because it can't work with a lot of fractions. Ex. Fractions $\frac{1}{4} \times \frac{1}{4} = \frac{1}{16}$ Not all true.

Lesson #6

What do you think of Dan's rules?
It makes sense because you just have to times the number by itself. When you get the answer it is higher than the number you times by itself. example: $7 = 49 \ (7 \times 7 = 49)$

Can you find any counter examples?

$\left(\frac{1}{5}\right) \ \frac{1}{5} \times \frac{1}{5} = \frac{1}{25}$ $\left(\frac{1}{7}\right) \ \frac{1}{7} \times \frac{1}{7} = \frac{1}{49}$

$\left(\frac{1}{8}\right) \ \frac{1}{8} \times \frac{1}{8} = \frac{1}{64}$ $\left(\frac{1}{2}\right) \ \frac{1}{2} \times \frac{1}{2} = \frac{1}{4}$

product is smaller than original number.

Dan's rule will work only if the number is 2 or higher than 2. Example: $2 = 4 \ (2 \times 2 = 4)$ lowest

Lesson #7

Dan's 2nd Rule →

"The cube of any number is always larger than the original."

Original #	Cube #
2	8
2.2	10.648
3	27
3.5	42.875
4	64

Dan's rule does make sense, because if you multiply a number by itself and by itself again the number will be larger than the number you started off with, for example:

$$5^3 = 5 \times 5 \times 5 = 125$$

13 → (13)×(13)×(13) = 2197
1.5 → (1.5)(1.5)(1.5) = 3375
7 → (7)(7)(7) = 343
21 → (21)(21)(21) = 9261
1 → (1)(1)(1) = 1   no-counterexample
0 → (0)(0)(0) = 0   "   "
-2 → (-2)(-2)(-2) = -8   "   "
$\frac{1}{4}$ → $\left(\frac{1}{4}\right)\left(\frac{1}{4}\right)\left(\frac{1}{4}\right) = \frac{1}{64}$ "

I changed my mind!

Lesson #9

Three Stacks

"The sum of 3 consecutive integers is divisible by 3."

Justification ➔ 23 24 25
62 63 64

$23 + 24 + 25 = 72$

$62 + 63 + 64 = 189$

$3\overline{)72}$

$3\overline{)189}$

$\frac{18}{9}$

(L) $^{1\,left}_{over}$ (B) $^{2\,left}_{over}$ (R) $^{3\,left}_{over}$ rectan.
÷ by

$7 + 12 = 19$

Three Stacks

"The sum of 3 consecutive integers is divisible by 3."

Justification:

18, 19, 20

21, 22, 23

29, 30, 31

$\begin{array}{r}18\\+19\\20\\\hline 57\end{array}$ $\begin{array}{r}19\\3\overline{)57}\\3\end{array}$

$\begin{array}{r}21\\22\\+23\\\hline 66\end{array}$ $\begin{array}{r}22\\3\overline{)66}\end{array}$

$\begin{array}{r}29\\30\\31\\\hline 90\end{array}$ $\begin{array}{r}30\\3\overline{)90}\end{array}$

rectangle
÷ by 3

7   12   19

L   R   L

Write a mathematical Argument

"whenever you add 3 consecutive whole numbers together, the sum will be divisible by 3."

Exmp: $\begin{array}{r}34\\+35\\36\\\hline 105\end{array}$ $\begin{array}{r}35\\3\overline{)105}\\9\\\hline 15\end{array}$

Everytime (mostly) when you do consecutive numbers you'll usually get the answer that is your second number. Also with the "Three Stack" numbers it'll be divisible by three because the stacks are three and it'll always fit into itself. (#3)

LESSON 1
Use Cubes to Model Calculations

1.

Solution	Cubes Used
$6 + (-3) = 3$	$6 + (-3)$ Remove zero-pairs. Answer
$-5 - (-4) = -1$	-5 Take away -4. Answer
$5 - (-3) = 8$	Start with 5. Add zero-pairs. Take away -3. Answer
$-4 + (-2) = -6$	Answer
$-6 - 3 = -9$	Start with -6. Add zero-pairs. Take away 3. Answer
$-3 - (-5) = 2$	Start with -3. Add zero-pairs. Take away -5. Answer

Solution	Cubes Used
$5 + (-7) = -2$	Start with 5. Add -7. Remove zero-pairs. Answer
$-4 - 2 = -6$	Start with -4. Add zero-pairs. Take away 2. Answer
$2 - (-1) = 3$	Start with 2. Add a zero-pair. Take away -1. Answer
$-4 + 7 = 3$	Start with -4. Add 7. Remove zero-pairs. Answer

Look for Counterexamples

1. Counterexample is $8 + (-3) = 5$.

2. true

3. Counterexample is $(-3) - (-5) = 2$. (Hyun's rule can sometimes be true, as with $-5 - (-3) = -2$.)

4. Counterexample is any addition of decimals where the decimals are different numbers, as with $-0.231 + 0.6 = 0.369$.

5. Counterexample is $\frac{3}{8} - (-\frac{1}{4}) = \frac{5}{8}$.

6. true

7. True. You may have to remove some zero-pairs, but you will never need to add additional zero-pairs to an addition problem.

Solving Sample Problems

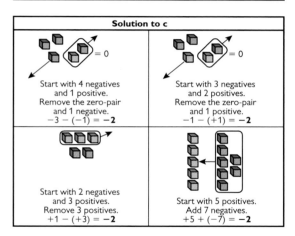

Solution to a	Solution to b
Start with 5 negatives. Subtract 3 negatives. $-5 - (-3) = -2$	Start with 1 negative and 4 positives. Add 5 negatives. $3 + (-5) = -2$

Solution to c	
Start with 4 negatives and 1 positive. Remove the zero-pair and 1 negative. $-3 - (-1) = -2$	Start with 3 negatives and 2 positives. Remove the zero-pair and 1 positive. $-1 - (+1) = -2$
Start with 2 negatives and 3 positives. Remove 3 positives. $+1 - (+3) = -2$	Start with 5 positives. Add 7 negatives. $+5 + (-7) = -2$

Use Cubes to Create Equations

1. **a.** $-3 + (-1) = -4$

   Start with 3 negatives. Add 1 negative.

   b. $-1 + (-3) = -4$

   Start with 2 negatives and 1 positive. Remove the zero-pair. Add 3 negatives.

   c. $1 + (-5) = -4$

   Start with 1 negative and 2 positives. Remove the zero-pair. Add 5 negatives.

   d. $3 + (-7) = -4$

   Start with 3 positives. Add 7 negatives.

2. **a.** $-4 + 3 = -1$

   Start with 4 negatives. Add 3 positives.

   b. $-2 - (-1) = -1$

   Start with 3 negatives and 1 positive. Remove the zero-pair. Take away 1 negative.

   c. $0 + (-1) = -1$

   Start with 2 negatives and 2 positives. Remove both zero-pairs. Add 1 negative.

   d. $2 + (-3) = -1$

   Start with 1 negative and 3 positives. Remove the zero-pair. Add 3 negatives.

   e. $4 + (-5) = -1$

   Start with 4 positives. Add 5 negatives.

3. **a.** $-5 - (-4) = -1$

   Start with 5 negatives. Take away 4 negatives.

   b. $-3 - (-2) = -1$

   Start with 4 negatives and 1 positive. Remove the zero-pair. Take away 2 negatives.

   c. $-1 + 0 = -1$

   Start with 3 negatives and 2 positives. Remove the zero-pairs. Add nothing.

   d. $1 + (-2) = -1$

   Start with 2 negatives and 3 positives. Remove the zero-pairs. Add 2 negatives.

   e. $3 + (-4) = -1$

   Start with 1 negative and 4 positives. Remove the zero-pair. Add 4 negatives.

   f. $5 + (-6) = -1$

   Start with 5 positives. Add 6 negatives.

ADDITIONAL SOLUTIONS

Subtraction Puzzles

Puzzle 1

Second Number

−	−1	5	4	−2
2	3	−3	−2	4
−3	−2	−8	−7	−1
0	1	−5	−4	2
−6	−5	−11	−10	−4

First Number

Puzzle 2

Second Number

−	−5	9	−2	−9
4	9	−5	6	13
−9	−4	−18	−7	0
−3	2	−12	−1	6
6	11	−3	8	15

First Number

LESSON 8
Create a Powers Chart

The Powers Chart

	$\square^1$	$\square^2$	$\square^3$	$\square^4$	$\square^5$	$\square^6$
1	1	1	1	1	1	1
2	2	4	8	16	32	64
3	3	9	27	81	243	729
4	4	16	64	256	1,024	4,096
5	5	25	125	625	3,125	15,625
6	6	36	216	1,296	7,776	46,656
7	7	49	343	2,401	16,807	117,649
8	8	64	512	4,096	32,768	262,144
9	9	81	729	6,561	59,049	531,441

LESSON 10
Investigate the Necessary Machines

1. Each set of machines can be given in any order.

   $15 = 3, 5$

   $28 = 2, 2, 7$

   $36 = 2, 2, 3, 3$

   $65 = 5, 13$

   $84 = 2, 2, 3, 7$

2. for 15: could use 1, 15

   for 28: could use 1, 14, or 28

   for 36: could use 1, 4, 6, 9, 12, 18, or 36

   for 65: could use 1, 65

   for 84: could use 1, 4, 6, 12, 14, 21, 28, 42, 84

3. This question is really asking what numbers between 1 and 100 have five prime factors; a factor may repeat.

   for five machines:

   $32 = 2, 2, 2, 2, 2$

   $48 = 2, 2, 2, 2, 3$

   $72 = 2, 2, 2, 3, 3$

   $80 = 2, 2, 2, 2, 5$

4. The greatest number of machines (or prime factors) a number from 1 to 100 can have is six.

   There are two possible solutions:

   $64 = 2, 2, 2, 2, 2, 2$

   $96 = 2, 2, 2, 2, 2, 3$

Solutions: Lesson 1

1. 4
2. 2
3. −3
4. −2
5. a zero-pair
6. one positive cube
7. −3
8. −2 − 1; −3
9. 2; Check students' drawings.
10. 8; Check students' drawings.
11. −5; Check students' drawings.
12. −3; Check students' drawings.
13. −10; Check students' drawings.
14. Answers will vary.
15. true
16. Counterexamples will vary. Rewrite: If you subtract a positive fraction from a positive fraction, you will sometimes get a number smaller than $\frac{3}{4}$.
17. Kate is right. Since the theory is that the sum of a positive number and a negative number is *always* positive, a single counterexample is sufficient to disprove the theory.

Homework 1

Statements About Signs

Applying Skills

For items 1–8, a pink square represents a positive cube and a green square represents a negative cube.

1. What number do these cubes show?

2. What number do these cubes show?

3. What number do these cubes show?

For items 4–8, use the pictures of cubes shown to solve a subtraction problem.

4. What number do the cubes show?

5. What has been added?

6. What has been removed?

7. What number is shown by the remaining cubes?

8. What was the subtraction problem? What is the answer?

For items 9–13, solve each problem by drawing pictures of cubes.

9. 3 + (−1)   10. 5 − (−3)

11. −2 + (−3)   12. −4 − (−1)

13. −6 − 4

Extending Concepts

14. Make up a problem with a positive answer which can be solved using cubes. To solve the problem, you will need to add some zero-pairs to your cubes. Draw the cubes to illustrate the problem.

For items 15–16, tell whether each statement is always true. If it is not always true, find a counterexample. Then rewrite the rule so that it is always true.

15. If you add a positive proper fraction and a negative proper fraction, you will always get a number smaller than 1.

16. If you subtract a positive fraction from a positive fraction, you will always get a number smaller than $\frac{3}{4}$.

Writing

17. Answer the letter to Dr. Math.

> Dear Dr. Math,
> My theory was: "The sum of a positive number and a negative number is always positive." I found 27 examples that worked. My friend Kate found one counterexample. So I figured 27 to 1, my theory must be good.
> But Kate said she only needed one counterexample to disprove my theory. Is this true?
> Positively Exhausted

Counterexamples and Cube Combinations

Applying Skills

For items 1–8, solve each problem and write the entire equation.

1. $3 + (-2)$ **2.** $7 - (-5)$ **3.** $-8 + (-2)$

4. $-3 - 8$ **5.** $4 + (-2) + (-3)$

6. $-5 + 3 - 6$ **7.** $6 - 2 - (-1)$

8. $4 + (-2) - 3 + (-9)$

9. Each number in the tables below is found subtracting the number in the top row from the number in the leftmost column. Copy each puzzle and fill in all the missing values.

−	−2	3	−4	8
1				
5		2		
−6				
0				

−	−3	4		
−2				
7		3	5	
				−3
			0	3

Extending Concepts

10. What combinations of four cubes can you come up with? For each combination, make up an addition or subtraction problem for which the answer is −4.

11. Find three different combinations of cubes, each representing the number −7. For each one, make up a problem for which the answer is 4.

12. If you add a positive number and a negative number, how can you tell whether the answer will be positive, negative, or zero?

13. Suppose you start with the number −3 and add a positive number. What can you say about the positive number if the answer is positive? negative? zero?

14. If you add two positive numbers and one negative number, will the answer always be positive? If not, how can you tell whether the answer will be positive, negative, or zero?

Making Connections

The *emu* is a large flightless bird of Australia. The *paradoxical frog* of South America is so-called because the adult frog is smaller than the tadpole. Tell whether each statement in 15–19 is always true. If the statement is not always true, give a counterexample.

15. Some birds can't fly.

16. No bird can fly.

17. All birds can fly.

18. In every species, the adult is bigger than the young.

19. There is no species in which the adult is bigger than the young.

Homework

Solutions: Lesson 2

1. 1 **2.** 12 **3.** −10

4. −11 **5.** −1 **6.** −8

7. 5 **8.** −10

9.

−	−2	3	−4	8
1	3	−2	5	−7
5	7	2	9	−3
−6	−4	−9	−2	−14
0	2	−3	4	−8

−	−3	4	2	−1
−2	1	−6	−4	−1
7	10	3	5	8
−4	−1	−8	−6	−3
2	5	−2	0	3

10. 4 positive cubes; 3 positive cubes, 1 negative cube; 2 positive cubes, 2 negative cubes; 1 positive cube, 3 negative cubes; 4 negative cubes; Problems will vary.

11. Answers will vary.

12. If the positive number is greater than the magnitude of the negative number, the answer will be positive; if the positive number is equal to the magnitude of the negative number, the answer will be zero; if the positive number is less than the magnitude of the negative number, the answer will be negative.

13. It is greater than 3; It is less than 3; It is equal to 3.

14. No; If the sum of the two positive numbers is greater than the magnitude of the negative number, the answer will be positive; If the sum of the two positive numbers is less than the magnitude of the negative number, the answer will be negative; If the sum of the two positive numbers is equal to the magnitude of the negative number, the answer will be zero.

15. true

16. Not always true; Many counterexamples are possible.

17. Not always true; The emu is one possible counterexample, others are possible.

18. Not always true; The paradoxical frog is one possible counterexample.

19. Not always true; Many counterexamples are possible.

Solutions: Lesson 3

1.

2. (circles with shaded and unshaded squares)

3. (four ovals each with three squares)

4. -40 5. -3 6. 3

7. 56 8. -4 9. 2.5

10. -2

11. a. One possible path:
$3 \times 2 \times (-1) \times (-4) \times 5 \times (-2)$.

b. It is possible to use all the numbers for the longest path by starting at 2 and connecting them in this order: 2, 3, −3, 2, −1, −4, 4, 5, −2, 3. (Other orders may be possible.) The product is 17,280.

12. a. There are many possible answers. Three are shown here:

$5 \times (-2) \div 4 \div 2 = -1.25$

$-4 \times (-2) \times (-1) \div 3 \div 2 = -1.33$

$2 \div (-2) \times 3 \div 2 = -1.5$

b. There are many possible answers. Three are shown here:

$5 \times (-2) \div (-2) \div 3 \div (-1) \div (-3) = 0.555\ldots$

$-4 \times 2 \times (-1) \div 3 \div 4 \div 2 = 0.333\ldots$

$2 \times (-1) \div (-3) = 0.666\ldots$

13. Answers will vary.

More Cases to Consider

Applying Skills

The multiplication 3×2 can be shown as 3 groups of 2.

Draw cubes similar to the ones above to show each multiplication in items 1–3. Use shaded squares to represent negative numbers.

1. 2×4 **2.** $3 \times (-5)$ **3.** 4×3

Solve each problem in items 4–10.

4. $5 \times (-8)$ **5.** $6 \div (-2)$

6. $-9 \div (-3)$ **7.** $-8 \times (-7)$

8. $6 \times (-2) \div 3$ **9.** $-5 \times 4 \div (-8)$

10. $-4 \div 4 \times (-10) \div (-5)$

Extending Concepts

In items 11 and 12, look for different paths in the puzzles that equal some result. For each path you find, write an equation. You may move in any direction along the dotted lines, but you may only use each number once.

11. A path that equals 24 is shown on this puzzle. You may use only multiplication.

Multiplication Puzzle

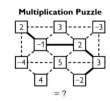

$= ?$

a. What path can you find that equals -240?

b. What is the longest path you can find? What does it equal?

12. In the puzzle below, you may use either multiplication or division. At each step, you choose which operation you want to use. You must use each operation at least once, and your path must start in the top row and end in the bottom row.

Multiplication and Division Puzzle

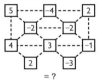

$= ?$

a. What path can you find that gives you an answer between -1 and -2?

b. What path can you find that gives you a positive answer smaller than 1?

Writing

13. Make up your own puzzle that uses multiplication, division, addition, and subtraction. Write two questions to go with your puzzle and make an answer key for each question.

Rules to Operate By

Applying Skills

For each subtraction problem in items 1–6, write an equivalent addition problem. For each addition problem, write an equivalent subtraction problem.

1. $8 - (-6)$ **2.** $9 - 2$ **3.** $7 + (-11)$

4. $10 - (-1)$ **5.** $3 + (-12)$ **6.** $4 + (-6)$

7. Using any pair of the numbers $5, -5, 8,$ and -8, write four different addition or subtraction problems that have the answer -13.

For items 8–9, use $-6, -1, 2, -9$, addition, and subtraction to solve each problem.

8. What problem can you find with the smallest possible answer?

9. What problem can you find for which the answer is zero?

10. Using the numbers $-6, \frac{1}{2}, -2,$ and 4, and any three operations, what problem can you find for which the answer lies between -2 and 0?

Extending Concepts

To answer items 11–12 use the puzzle shown. You may use addition, subtraction, multiplication, or division. You must use each operation at least once, and your path must start in the top row and end in the bottom row. Remember, you may move in any direction along the dotted lines, but you may only use each number once.

11. What path gives an answer between 1 and 2?

12. What path gives an answer greater than 100?

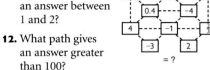
= ?

13. What statement could you write for which $2 + (-6) = -4$ is the counterexample?

Tell whether each statement in items 14–15 is always true or not always true. If it is not always true, find a counterexample.

14. If you subtract a negative fraction from a positive fraction, you will always get a number greater than $\frac{1}{4}$.

15. The product of two numbers will always be greater than the sum of the same two numbers.

Making Connections

For items 16 and 17, use the following information:

The Dead Sea is a salt lake lying on the Israel-Jordan border. At 1,292 feet below sea level, its surface is the lowest point on earth. At 29,028 feet, the top of Mount Everest is the highest point on earth.

16. Write a subtraction equation to find the elevation difference between the top of Mount Everest and the surface of the Dead Sea.

17. Write an equivalent addition equation.

Homework

Solutions: Lesson 4

1. $8 + 6$

2. $9 + (-2)$

3. $7 - 11$

4. $10 + 1$

5. $3 - 12$

6. $4 - 6$

7. $-5 + (-8) = -13$; $-5 - 8 = -13$; $-8 - 5 = -13$; $-8 + (-5) = -13$

8. To obtain the smallest possible answer, the $-6, -1,$ and -9 should be added and the 2 subtracted. One possible problem: $-6 + (-1) + (-9) - 2 = -18$. The order may vary.

9. Answers may vary. Possible answer: $-6 + (-1) - 2 - (-9) = 0$

10. Answers will vary. Possible answer: $-6 \times \frac{1}{2} + (-2) + 4 = -1$

11. Answers will vary. Possible answer: $(3 - (-\frac{1}{2}) + 0.4) \times (-1) \div (-3) = 1.3$

12. Answers will vary. Possible answer: $(3 \div (-\frac{1}{2}) + (-2) - 0.4) \times 4 \times (-3) = 100.8$

13. Two possible statements for which $2 + (-6) = -4$ is a counterexample are: "A positive plus a negative will always be positive," and "Adding a smaller number to a larger number will make the answer greater than either number."

14. Not always true; Counterexamples will vary.

15. Not always true; Counterexamples will vary.

16. $29,028 - (-1,292) = 30,320$ ft

17. $29,028 + 1,292 = 30,320$ ft

Solutions: Lesson 5

1. $7^2 = 49$
2. $12^2 = 144$
3. $16^2 = 256$
4. $29^2 = 841$
5. 7
6. 9
7. 14
8. 22
9. 32
10. 38
11. 11
12. 23
13. 37
14. 61
15. 6th and 7th perfect squares
16. 9th and 10th perfect squares
17. 15th and 16th perfect squares
18. 54th and 55th perfect squares
19. 181st and 182nd perfect squares
20. 18th and 19th perfect squares
21. −6
22. −8
23. −12
24. −18
25. −33
26. −42
27. The increases are 4, 8, 12; The pattern is 4, 8, 12, 16, 20, 24…; Between the 9th and 10th figures the increase will be 36.
28. Answers will vary. One possibility is the increase in the number of dots between Figure n and Figure $n + 1$ is $4n$; 400
29. The number of dots in Figure n is $n^2 + (n − 1)^2$; $40^2 + 39^2 = 3,121.$
30. 1,513

Perfect Pattern Predictions

Applying Skills

For items 1–4, write each square using exponents and find their values.

1. 7 squared
2. 12 squared
3. 16 squared
4. 29 squared

For items 5–10, find each square root.

5. $\sqrt{49}$
6. $\sqrt{81}$
7. $\sqrt{196}$
8. $\sqrt{484}$
9. $\sqrt{1,024}$
10. $\sqrt{1,444}$

For items 11–14, find the increase between each pair of perfect squares.

11. 5th and 6th perfect squares
12. 11th and 12th perfect squares
13. 18th and 19th perfect squares
14. 30th and 31st perfect squares

For items 15–20, between which two perfect squares will the increase be:

15. 13?
16. 19?
17. 31?
18. 109?
19. 363?
20. 37?

Extending Concepts

For items 21–26, find each square root.

21. $-\sqrt{36}$
22. $-\sqrt{64}$
23. $-\sqrt{144}$
24. $-\sqrt{324}$
25. $-\sqrt{1,089}$
26. $-\sqrt{1,764}$

For items 27–29, use the pictures shown to answer the questions.

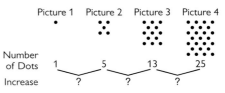

27. Find the increase in the number of dots between each of the figures shown. What pattern do you notice? What will be the increase in the number of dots between the 9th and 10th figures?

28. Describe a rule you could use to find the increase in the number of dots between any two figures. What will the increase be between the 100th and 101st figures?

29. The number of dots in the third figure is $3^2 + 2^2$ or 13. The number of dots in the 4th figure is $4^2 + 3^2$ or 25. What pattern do you notice? How many dots will be in the 40th figure?

Making Connections

30. The pyramid of Khufu in Egypt was built in 2680 B.C. as a burial tomb for the king. It has a square base measuring 756 feet on each side. The formula for the area of a square is s^2, where s is the length of a side. If each side of the pyramid was one foot longer, how much greater would the area of the base be?

Counterexamples and Special Cases

Applying Skills

For items 1–6, tell whether the square of each number is larger or smaller than the number itself. Do not calculate the square.

1. 5   **2.** 0.9   **3.** $\frac{1}{5}$ **4.** -18 **5.** $\frac{2}{3}$ **6.** -0.1

For items 7–9, show each multiplication by drawing a sketch, then give the result.

7. $\frac{1}{3} \times \frac{1}{2}$ **8.** $\frac{1}{2} \times \frac{1}{2}$ **9.** $2 \times \frac{1}{3}$

10. Copy and fill in a table like the one shown. Estimate the square root of each number in the table. Write down your estimate and then test it by squaring it. Repeat this process two more times. Then use your calculator to calculate how much your best estimate differed from the answer shown on the calculator.

	What is the square root of:	Estimate 1	Estimate 2	Estimate 3	By how much did your best estimate differ?
a.	43				
b.	86				
c.	306				
d.	829				

Extending Concepts

For items 11–14, consider the following rule: "The square root of a number is always smaller than the original number."

11. Give three counterexamples to the rule.

12. Test whether the rule works for each of these special cases: negative numbers, proper fractions, 0, 1, and positive numbers greater than 1. Explain any special cases where the rule does not work.

13. Write a correct version of the rule.

14. Why do you think that 0 and 1 are often tested as special cases?

Writing

15. You learned in class that the square of a proper fraction is smaller than the original fraction. Use this theory to explain the meaning of counterexamples and special cases. You may want to give examples in your explanation.

Solutions: Lesson 6

1. larger   2. smaller

3. smaller   4. larger

5. smaller   6. larger

7. $\frac{1}{6}$; Check students' drawings.

8. $\frac{1}{4}$; Check students' drawings.

9. $\frac{2}{3}$; Check students' drawings.

10. Check students' estimates; Actual square roots to two decimal places are:

     a. 6.56   **b.** 9.27

     c. 17.49   **d.** 28.79

11. Answers will vary.

12. no; no; no; no; yes. Negative numbers: cannot take the square root of a negative number; proper fractions: square root is larger than the original number; 0 and 1: square root is equal to the original number; numbers greater than 1: the rule works.

13. The square root of any number greater than 1 is smaller than the original number.

14. Answers may vary. Possible answer: 0 and 1 have special properties which means that rules that work for most other numbers may not work for 0 or 1. For example, 1 is the multiplicative identity and 0 has the property that when any number is multiplied by zero, the result is zero.

15. Answers will vary.

Solutions: Lesson 7

1. 27 2. 1,331 3. -64

4. -729 5. 5 6. -10

7. perfect cube

8. not a perfect cube

9. perfect cube

10. not a perfect cube

11. perfect cube

12. perfect cube

13. Answers will vary.

14. No; no; no; no; yes; proper fractions: The cube is smaller than the square; 0 and 1: The cube and the square are equal; negative numbers: The cube is smaller than the square because the cube is negative and the square is positive; numbers greater than 1: the rule holds.

15. The cube of any number greater than 1 is greater than the square of the same number.

16. Check students' estimates. Actual cube roots are shown to two decimal places.

   a. between 3 and 4 (3.68)

   b. between 5 and 6 (5.85)

   c. between 8 and 9 (8.04)

17. No; If a number has a negative cube root, then it must be a negative number. It is not possible to take the square root of a negative number.

18. Venus: $d^3 = 300,763$; $T^2 = 50,625$; $\dfrac{d^3}{T^2} = 5.94$

   Mercury: $d^3 = 46,656$; $T^2 = 7,744$; $\dfrac{d^3}{T^2} = 6.02$

   Yes, values of $\dfrac{d^3}{T^2}$ are approximately the same for all three planets.

Root Relationships

Homework 7

Applying Skills

Calculate items 1–6. To figure out the cube roots, you may want to use a calculator to guess and check.

1. 3^3 **2.** 11^3 **3.** $(-4)^3$

4. $(-9)^3$ **5.** the cube root of 125

6. the cube root of $-1,000$

For items 7–12, tell whether each number is a perfect cube.

7. 64 **8.** 16 **9.** -8

10. 25 **11.** 343 **12.** 1,728

For items 13–15, consider the following rule: "The cube of any number is greater than the square of the same number."

13. Give three counterexamples to the rule.

14. Test whether the rule works for each of these special cases: proper fractions, 0, 1, negative numbers, and positive numbers greater than 1. If there are some special cases for which the rule does not work, explain why not.

15. Write a new correct version of the rule.

Extending Concepts

16. Copy and fill in a table like the one shown. For each cube root, think about the two whole-number cube roots it might lie between. Write your answer in the second column. Estimate the cube root to the nearest hundredth. Write your answer in the third column.

	What is the cube root of:	Lies between cube roots:	Estimate
a.	50		
b.	200		
c.	520		

17. Is it possible to find a number with a negative cube root and a positive square root? If so, give an example. If not, explain why not.

Making Connections

For item 18, use the following:

Kepler's third law states that for all planets orbiting the sun, the cube of the average distance to the sun divided by the square of the period (the time to complete one revolution around the sun) is about the same.

18. Look at the table shown. Here is an example of the calculations for Earth:

$$d^3 = 93^3 = 804,357$$

$$T^2 = 365^2 = 133,225$$

$$\frac{d^3}{T^2} = \frac{804,357}{133,225} = 6.04$$

Is the law true for Earth, Venus, and Mercury?

Planet	Average distance to sun in millions of miles (d)	Period in days (T)
Earth	93	365
Venus	67	225
Mercury	36	88

A Powerful Argument

Applying Skills

Calculate items 1–10. To figure out the cube roots, you may want to use the calculator to guess and check.

1. 11^4 **2.** 7^3 **3.** 8^6

4. 4^5 **5.** 3^7 **6.** $\sqrt{529}$

7. the cube root of 729

8. $\sqrt{289}$ **9.** $\sqrt{1,225}$

10. the cube root of -1331

Without using a calculator, identify each number in items 11–19 that you know is a perfect square. Tell why you know.

11. 4^5 **12.** 5^6 **13.** 6^3

14. 8^7 **15.** 2^{10} **16.** 3^9

17. 9^3 **18.** 7^8 **19.** 11^4

20. Use your calculator to calculate each power in items 11–19.

21. Use the square root key on your calculator to find the square root for each number in items 11–19. Identify which of the numbers is a perfect square.

Extending Concepts

22. Copy the table shown. Which rows and columns in the table do you think are perfect cubes? How can you tell?

The Powers Chart

	$\square^1$	$\square^2$	$\square^3$	$\square^4$	$\square^5$	$\square^6$
6						
7						
8						

23. Complete the table by raising each number to the exponent at the top of the column.

24. Use guess-and-check and your calculator to check which numbers in the table are perfect cubes and circle them.

25. Someone made this mathematical argument: $x^a \times x^b = x^{a+b}$. What do you think about it?

Making Connections

Use this information for items 26 and 27.

Jainism is a religious system of India which arose in the 6th century B.C. and is practiced today by about 2 million people. According to Jaina cosmology, the population of the world is a number which can be divided by two 96 times. This number can be written in exponent form as 2^{96}.

26. Is 2^{96} a perfect square? How can you tell?

27. Is 2^{96} a perfect cube? How can you tell?

Homework

Solutions: Lesson 8

1. 14,641   2. 343
3. 262,144   4. 1,024
5. 2,187   6. 23
7. 9   8. 17
9. 35   10. −11

11–19. Items **11, 12, 15, 17, 18,** and **19** are perfect squares. Reasons will vary, but one possibility is that any number raised to an even power will be a perfect square and any perfect square raised to an integer power will also be a perfect square.

20. 1,024; 15,625; 216; 2,097,152; 1,024; 19,683; 729; 5,764,801; 14,641

21. 32; 125; 14.70 (not a perfect square); 1,448.15 (not a perfect square); 32; 140.30 (not a perfect square); 27; 2,401; 121

22. Last row, columns $\square^3$ and $\square^6$ are perfect cubes.

23.

	$\square^1$	$\square^2$	$\square^3$	$\square^4$	$\square^5$	$\square^6$
6	6	36	216	1,296	7,776	46,656
7	7	49	343	2,401	16,807	117,649
8	8	64	512	4,096	32,768	262,144

24. Last row, columns $\square^3$ and $\square^6$ are perfect cubes.

25. Answers will vary.

26. Yes; 96 is even.

27. Yes; 96 is divisible by 3.

Solutions: Lesson 9

1. L number

2. b number

3. rectangle number

4. L number

5. b number

6. rectangle number

7. L number; b number; b number; rectangle number; b number; L number; rectangle number; L number

8. rectangle number

9. b number

10. L number

11. L number

12. rectangle number; an L number

13. b number; a rectangle number; yes; Answers will vary.

14. II number

15. No; If you add four consecutive integers, you will get a II number which is not divisible by 4.

16. Yes; Since the sum of any three consecutive integers is divisible by 3, the sum divided by 3 will be an integer.

Three-Stack Shape Sums

Applying Skills

In the 3-stacks model, cubes are stacked in columns with a height of 3 cubes. The rightmost column may contain 1 cube (L numbers), 2 cubes (b numbers), or 3 cubes (rectangle numbers).

4   5   6

For items 1–6, draw a sketch showing how you could make each number using the 3-stacks model. Tell which kind of number each number is: a rectangle number, a b number, or an L number.

1. 7   **2.** 8   **3.** 12

4. 16   **5.** 17   **6.** 18

7. What kind of number is 22? 35? 41? 57? 71? 103? 261? 352?

For items 8–11, complete this question: What kind of number is the sum of:

8. an L number and a b number?

9. a b number and a rectangle number?

10. a rectangle number and an L number?

11. a b number and a b number?

Extending Concepts

For items 12–13, suppose the smallest of three consecutive integers is a b number.

12. What kind of number is the middle number? the largest number?

13. What kind of number do you get if you add the two smaller numbers? all three numbers? Is the sum of the three numbers divisible by 3? How do you know?

In the 4-stacks model, cubes are stacked in columns with a height of 4 cubes. The rightmost column may contain 1, 2, 3, or 4 cubes as shown. Use the 4-stacks model to answer items 14–15.

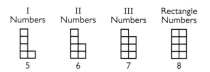

| I Numbers | II Numbers | III Numbers | Rectangle Numbers |
| 5 | 6 | 7 | 8 |

14. What kind of number do you get if you add a I number, a II number, a III number, and a rectangle number?

15. Is the sum of four consecutive integers always divisible by 4? Use your answer to item **14** to explain your answer.

Making Connections

16. The *mean* of a set of numbers is found by adding the numbers and dividing by the number of numbers. Do you think that the mean of three consecutive integers is always an integer? Use what you have learned in this lesson to explain your thinking.

MAKING MATHEMATICAL ARGUMENTS   HOMEWORK 9

A Stretching Problem

Applying Skills

For items 1–6, remember that at the Bubble Gum Factory, 1-inch lengths of gum are stretched to lengths from 1 to 100 inches by putting them through a stretching machine. There are 100 stretching machines. Which of the following machines are unnecessary?

1. 5   **2.** 14   **3.** 19

4. 31   **5.** 37   **6.** 51

For items 7–12, tell what necessary machines give these lengths:

7. 12 inches   **8.** 30 inches   **9.** 44 inches

10. 66 inches   **11.** 72 inches   **12.** 18 inches

For items 13–15, find the prime factors of each number.

13. 18   **14.** 48   **15.** 75

16. How can you tell whether a number is divisible by 3? by 9? by 5?

Extending Concepts

For items 17–19, use the same stretching machine described for items 1–12.

17. If you use only necessary machines, for which of the lengths 1 to 100 inches would exactly four runs through a stretching machine be needed? Give the lengths and tell which machines would be needed for each one.

18. Suppose a particular length can be obtained by using the necessary machines 2, 2, 3, 7. If you could also use unnecessary machines, what other combinations of machines could be used to obtain the same length? How did you solve this problem?

19. Describe a method to identify all the prime numbers between 1 and 200. Explain why your method works.

Writing

20. Answer the letter to Dr. Math.

> Dear Dr. Math,
> We had to find all the prime numbers between 1 and 100. I think I noticed a pattern: All the odd numbers that were *not* prime were divisible by either 3, 5, or 7. So now I can tell whether *any* number is prime: If it's even, I eliminate it right away. If it's odd, I have to figure out whether it's divisible by 3, 5, or 7. If it's not divisible by any of them, then I know I've got a prime number. Has anyone else noticed this pattern? How should I explain why this is true?
> In My Prime

Solutions: Lesson 10

1. necessary   2. unnecessary
3. necessary   4. necessary
5. necessary   6. unnecessary
7. 2, 2, 3   8. 2, 3, 5
9. 2, 2, 11   10. 2, 3, 11
11. 2, 2, 2, 3, 3   12. 2, 3, 3
13. $2 \times 3 \times 3$ 14. $2 \times 2 \times 2 \times 2 \times 3$
15. $3 \times 5 \times 5$

16. If a number is divisible by 3, the sum of its digits is divisible by 3; If a number is divisible by 9, the sum of its digits is divisible by 9; If a number is divisible by 5, its last digit will be a 5 or a 0.

17. 16 in: 2, 2, 2, 2; 24 in: 2, 2, 2, 3; 36 in: 2, 2, 3, 3; 40 in: 2, 2, 2, 5; 54 in: 2, 3, 3, 3; 56 in: 2, 2, 2, 7; 60 in: 2, 2, 3, 5; 81 in: 3, 3, 3, 3; 84 in: 2, 2, 3, 7; 88 in: 2, 2, 2, 11; 90 in: 2, 3, 3, 5; 100 in: 2, 2, 5, 5

18. 84; 2, 42; 2, 2, 21; 2, 6, 7; 2, 3, 14; 3, 4, 7; 3, 28; 7, 12; 4, 21; 6, 14

19. Answers will vary.

20. This method happens to work for the numbers 1–100, but does not work in general. The fact that an odd number is not divisible by 3, 5, or 7 does not mean that it is a prime number; it could be divisible by larger prime numbers. The number 143, for example, is not divisible by 3, 5, or 7, but is divisible by both 11 and 13 and is therefore not a prime number. Also note that 2, the smallest positive even number, is a prime; it should not be eliminated.

Solutions: Lesson 11

1 time	2×	3×	4×	5×	6×	7×	8×	9×	10×
1	2	4	6	16	12		24		
	3	9	8		18				
	5	25	10		20				
	7		14						
	11		15						
	13		21						
	17		22						
	19								
	23								

1. 2×
2. 4×
3. 9×
4. 2×
5. 6×
6. 4×

7. 12×

8. 12×. It has 12 factors.

9. In the 5× column, the first three numbers greater than 100 are 625, 2,401, and 14,641. Only a perfect square has an odd number of factors. Numbers in the 5× column are squares of numbers in the 3× column, which in turn are squares of prime numbers.

10. They are prime numbers.

11. No; If a number is not a perfect square, then each of its factors can be paired with a distinct factor that multiply together to give the original number. For a perfect square there is one factor, namely the square root, that pairs with itself. So a perfect square has an odd number of factors and could appear in the 3× column; other numbers could not appear there.

12. 12 columns; 60, 72, 84, 90, 96

13. 4×; Answers will vary.

14. $2 \times 2 \times 2$; Doubling a number is equivalent to multiplying it by 2. Since 8 contains the factor 2 three times, doubling a number three times is equivalent to multiplying it by 8; 88.

15. Since 14 can be written as $8 + 4 + 2$, multiply the number by 8, multiply it by 4, and multiply it by 2 and add the results.

Homework 11

Pattern Appearances

Applying Skills

Use the table you created in class or copy and complete the table below to show how many times each number from 1 to 25 would appear on a Multiplication Chart if the chart went on to infinity.

1 time	2 times	3 times	4 times	5 times	6 times	7 times	8 times	9 times	10 times
1	2	4							
	3								
	5								

For items 1–7, write down which column of the table each number belongs in.

1. 31 **2.** 26 **3.** 36 **4.** 41 **5.** 52 **6.** 58 **7.** 60

Extending Concepts

Use your table to answer items 8–11.

8. In which column would 132 appear? Why?

9. Find three numbers greater than 100 which belong in the 5-times column. How did you find them?

10. What can you say about the numbers that appear in the 2-times column?

11. Is it possible for a number that is not a perfect square to appear in the 3-times column? Explain why or why not.

For items 12–13, suppose you listed all the numbers from 1 to 100 in your table.

12. How many columns would you need? Which number or numbers would appear in the rightmost column?

13. Which column would have the most numbers in it? Why?

Making Connections

For items 14–15, use the following information:

The Ancient Egyptians had their own system for multiplying numbers. Examples of their system are as follows: To multiply a number by 2, double it. To multiply a number by 4, double it twice. To multiply a number by 8, double it three times. To multiply by 12, since 12 can be written as $8 + 4$, multiply the number by 8 and by 4 and add the results.

14. What are the prime factors of 8? Why does it make sense that to multiply a number by 8, you would double it three times? Use this method to multiply 11 by 8 and describe the steps.

15. How do you think the Ancient Egyptians would have multiplied a number by 14?

12 Homework

The Final Arguments

Applying Skills

Use the table you created in class or copy and complete the table below to show how many times each number from 1 to 25 would appear on the Multiplication Chart if the chart went on to infinity. Use your table to answer items 1–5.

1 time	2 times	3 times	4 times	5 times	6 times	7 times	8 times	9 times	10 times
1	2	4							
	3								
	5								

1. The perfect squares 1, 4, 9, 16, and 25 all appear in a column headed by an odd number. Do you think that *all* perfect squares belong in a column headed by an odd number? If so, explain why you think so. If not, give a counterexample.

2. What is special about the perfect squares that appear in the 3-times column? Explain why this makes sense.

3. Are there any numbers in a column headed by an odd number that are not perfect squares? Why or why not?

4. Do you think that all perfect cubes, other than 1, belong in the 4-times column? If not, give a counterexample. What is special about the perfect cubes that appear in the 4-times column? Why does this make sense?

5. Summarize the patterns regarding perfect squares and perfect cubes in an accurate mathematical argument.

Extending Concepts

For items 6–8, test whether each statement about cube roots is true.

6. The cube root of any number is smaller than the original number if the original number is a positive fraction.

7. The cube root of any number is smaller than the original number if the original number is 0.

8. The cube root of any number is smaller than the original number if the original number is smaller than −1.

For items 9 and 10, test whether each statement about divisibility is true.

9. If you divide 10 by a positive fraction, the answer will be smaller than 10.

10. If you divide 10 by a negative number, the answer will be smaller than 10.

Writing

11. Write a paragraph explaining the steps that are involved in making an accurate and complete mathematical argument. Explain why each step is important. Which special cases might you test? Why?

Homework

Solutions: Lesson 12

1 time	2×	3×	4×	5×	6×	7×	8×	9×	10×
1	2	4	6	16	12		24		
	3	9	8		18				
	5	25	10		20				
	7		14						
	11		15						
	13		21						
	17		22						
	19								
	23								

1. Yes; If you list the factors by pairs that multiply together to give the original number, a perfect square will always have one pair that consists of the same number twice. Thus, any perfect square has an odd number of factors.

2. They are squares of prime numbers.

3. No; If a number is not a perfect square it must have an even number of factors, since each of its factors can be paired with a distinct factor that multiply together to give the original number.

4. No; $64 = 4^3$ belongs in the 7× column. Numbers in the 4× column are cubes of prime numbers. The cube of a prime number has four factors: 1, the prime number, the square of the prime number, and the cube of the prime number.

5. Every perfect square appears in a column headed by an odd number. Squares of prime numbers appear in the 3× column. If a number is not a perfect square it must appear in a column headed by an even number. Cubes of prime numbers appear in the 4× column.

6. no   7. no   8. no

9. no   10. yes

11. Answers will vary.

Making Mathematical Arguments
ASSESSMENT CHECKLIST

Name: _____ Period: _____ Date: _____

Lesson	Assignment Description	Assessment	Notes
Pre-assessment	What is involved in making a mathematical argument?		
Lesson 1	Statements About Signs		
Lesson 2	Counterexamples and Cube Combinations		
Lesson 3	More Cases to Consider		
Lesson 4	Rules to Operate By		
Phase One Skill Check	Skill Quiz 1 & Homework 1–4		
Lesson 5	Perfect Pattern Predictions		
Lesson 6	Counterexamples and Special Cases		
Lesson 7	Root Relationships		
Lesson 8	A Powerful Argument		
Phase Two Skill Check	Skill Quiz 2 & Homework 5–8		
Lesson 9	Three-Stack Shape Sums		
Lesson 10	A Stretching Problem		
Lesson 11	Pattern Appearances		
Lesson 12	The Final Arguments		
Phase Three Skill Check	Skill Quiz 3 & Homework 9–12		
Post-assessment	What is involved in making a mathematical argument?		

Comments:

PHASE ONE
Skill Quiz

In this quiz, an unshaded square represents a positive cube and a shaded square represents a negative cube.

For items **1–3**, what number is represented by each picture?

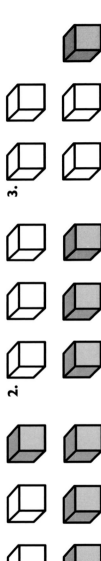

1.

2.

3.

For items **4–7**, solve each problem by drawing pictures of cubes.

4. $-4 + (-3)$ **5.** $-5 - (-2)$ **6.** $2 - (-4)$ **7.** $-4 - 3$

For items **8–16**, solve each problem.

8. $-7 + 2$ **9.** $-8 - 1$ **10.** $-1 - (-2)$

11. $5 \times (-6)$ **12.** $-6 \div (-2)$ **13.** $-5 - 3 + (-2)$

14. $-6 + 2 + (-4)$ **15.** $-8 \times (-7) \div (-2)$ **16.** $8 \div (-2) \times 3$

For each subtraction problem in items **17–19**, write an equivalent addition problem.

17. $2 - 6$ **18.** $3 - (-2)$ **19.** $-7 - (-11)$

20. What combinations of five cubes can you come up with? For each one, make up an addition or subtraction problem for which the answer is -3.

For items **21–23**, tell whether each statement is always true. If it is not always true, find a counterexample, then restate the rule so that it is always true.

21. If you add a negative number and a positive number, the answer will always be negative.

22. If you subtract a negative fraction from a positive fraction, the answer will always be positive.

23. If you add a negative fraction to a negative fraction, the answer will always be smaller than $-\frac{1}{8}$.

24. Look at the statements in the box below. Choose one that has at least one counterexample. Show the counterexample(s). Then rewrite the statement you chose so that it is always true.

> **Is It Always True?**
> Positive + Positive = Positive
> Positive + Negative = Negative
> Negative + Negative = Negative
> Positive − Positive = Positive
> Positive − Negative = Positive
> Negative − Positive = Positive
> Negative − Positive = Negative
> Negative − Negative = Negative

PHASE TWO
Skill Quiz

Calculate the problems in items 1–10.

1. 13^2 **2.** $(-29)^2$ **3.** $\sqrt{121}$ **4.** $\sqrt{676}$

5. 5^3 **6.** $(-14)^3$ **7.** $\sqrt[3]{512}$ **8.** $\sqrt[3]{-1,728}$

9. 7^4 **10.** 3^7

For items **11–12**, find the increase between each pair of perfect squares.

11. 7th and 8th perfect squares **12.** 15th and 16th perfect squares

For items **13–16**, between which two perfect squares will the increase be:

13. 7? **14.** 25? **15.** 133? **16.** 261?

For items **17–20**, predict whether the square of each number will be larger or smaller than the number itself. Explain how you can tell.

17. 0.1 **18.** −19 **19.** 55 **20.** $-\dfrac{2}{3}$

21. Copy and fill in a table like the one shown. Estimate the square root of each number in the table. Write down your estimate and then test the estimate by squaring it. Repeat this process two more times. Then use your calculator to calculate how much your best estimate differed from the answer shown on the calculator.

What Is the Square Root of:	Estimate 1	Estimate 2	Estimate 3	By How Much Did Your Best Estimate Differ?
a. 20				
b. 195				
c. 730				

For items **22–25**, consider the following rule: "The cube root of a number is always smaller than the square root of the same number."

22. Give three specific counterexamples to the rule.

23. Test whether the rule works for each of the following: negative numbers, proper fractions, 0, 1, and positive numbers greater than 1.

24. If there are some special cases of numbers for which the rule does not work, explain why not.

25. Write a new version of the rule that is correct and complete.

For items **26–31**, predict whether each number will be a perfect square. Explain how you can tell.

26. 3^5 **27.** 5^9 **28.** 8^5

29. 4^7 **30.** 11^6 **31.** 9^9

32. Predict whether each number in items **26–31** will be a perfect cube. Explain how you can tell.

33. Use your calculator to calculate each power in items **26–31**.

34. Use your calculator to tell whether each number in items **26–31** is a perfect square and whether it is a perfect cube.

PHASE THREE
Skill Quiz

For items **1–3**, draw a picture showing how you could make each number using the 3-stack model. Tell which kind of number each number is: a rectangle number, a b number, or an L number.

1. 9   **2.** 13   **3.** 14

4. What kind of number is 33? 251?

For items **5–6**, answer this question: What kind of number is the sum of:

5. a b number and an L number?   **6.** an L number and an L number?

At the Bubble Gum Factory, 1-inch lengths of gum are stretched to lengths from 1 to 100 inches by putting them through a stretching machine. There are 100 stretching machines. Machine 23, for example, will stretch a piece of gum to 23 times its original length.

Some of the machines are unnecessary because combinations of other machines could be used instead. Tell whether each machine in items **7–12** is necessary.

7. 19   **8.** 21   **9.** 37

10. 39   **11.** 59   **12.** 91

For items **13–16**, what necessary machines could you use to get the following lengths:

13. 27 in.?   **14.** 38 in.?   **15.** 52 in.?   **16.** 84 in.?

17. If you use only necessary machines, for which of the lengths 1 to 100 inches would exactly 6 runs through stretching machines be needed? Give the lengths and tell which machines would be needed for each one.

18. Copy and complete the table below to show how many times each number from 1–25 would appear on the Multiplication Chart if the chart went on to infinity. Use the table to answer items **19–27.**

1 time	2 times	3 times	4 times	5 times	6 times	7 times	8 times	9 times	10 times	
1	2	4								
	3									

For items **19–23**, tell which column of the table each number belongs in. Explain how you can tell.

19. 29   **20.** 49   **21.** 50

22. 61   **23.** 76

24. Find three numbers greater than 100 which belong in the 6-times column in the table you made. How did you find them?

25. If you listed all the numbers from 1 to 50 in the table you made, which column would have the most numbers in it?

26. What can you say about the numbers that appear in the 3-times column of your table? the numbers in the 2-times column?

27. If a number is a cube of a prime number, in which column of your table would it appear? Why does this make sense?

Student Assessment Criteria

PHASE ONE

Does my work show that I can...

- understand how subtracting a negative number and adding a positive number are related?

- find counterexamples?

- describe the rule for multiplying and dividing several signed numbers together?

- understand the meaning of the term *rule* in mathematics?

PHASE TWO

Does my work show that I can...

- understand patterns of perfect squares on a grid?

- state a rule about the patterns of perfect squares in rows or columns of the grid?

- describe methods used to figure out the rule and include counterexamples?

PHASE THREE
Student Assessment Criteria

Does my work show that I can...

- understand factors, primes, squares, and cubes?

- carefully choose a mathematical argument?

- state a rule about patterns in the Multiplication Chart?

- describe methods I used to figure out the rule and include counterexamples?

- explain special cases for which the rule does not work?

Dear Family,

Our class will be soon be starting a new mathematics unit called *Making Mathematical Arguments*. The unit begins with investigations of addition, subtraction, multiplication, and division with positive and negative numbers (also called "signed" numbers). Students will start by using cube-shaped blocks in two different colors to represent problems involving signed numbers. One color represents positive numbers and another color represents negative numbers. In the examples below, the unshaded cubes represent positive numbers and the shaded cubes represent negative numbers.

The problem $-3 + (-2)$, shown here, is represented by making a group of 3 negative cubes, then adding 2 more negative cubes to the pile. The result is -5.

In addition problems where the signs of the numbers are different, pairs of cubes that equal 0 are removed to find the solution. The problem $4 + (-2)$ is shown here.

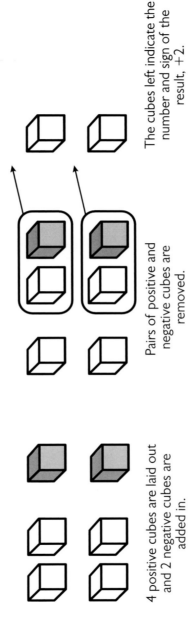

4 positive cubes are laid out and 2 negative cubes are added in.

Pairs of positive and negative cubes are removed.

The cubes left indicate the number and sign of the result, $+2$.

The cubes help students think about signed-number operations and explore statements about the rules for signed-number operations. Students will gain both a good understanding of the rules and an ability to solve signed-number problems with or without cubes.

The rest of the unit focuses on testing rules for special cases. Again, students will use cubes to explore patterns and rules involving square numbers, square roots, cubic numbers, and cube roots. Students will also look at patterns in prime numbers and factors. By the end of the unit, students will be ready to craft a "mathematical argument" of their own about a pattern they have discovered in the unit. The mathematical argument will describe a rule and use examples and counterexamples to define the set of numbers to which the rule applies.

Sincerely,

MAKING MATHEMATICAL ARGUMENTS
© Creative Publications • MathScape

Cube Calculations with Signed Numbers

You can model addition and subtraction of signed numbers using cubes in two colors. In the examples on this page, the white cubes represent positive numbers and the shaded cubes represent negative numbers.

Showing Signed Numbers with Cubes

Here are some different ways to show the number 5 using cubes.

5 positives

6 positives and 1 negative

(zero-pair)

7 positives and 2 negatives

What are some other ways to show 5 using cubes?

Using Cubes to Model Addition and Subtraction of Signed Numbers

Here are some examples of how to use cubes to solve addition and subtraction problems involving signed numbers. The figures below show how to use cubes to solve 4 + (−2).

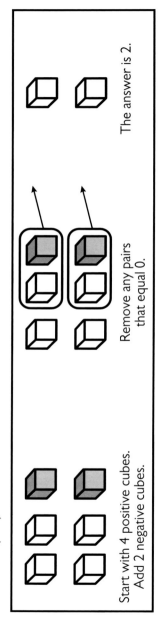

Start with 4 positive cubes.
Add 2 negative cubes.

Remove any pairs that equal 0.

The answer is 2.

The figures below show how to use cubes to solve 4 − (−2).

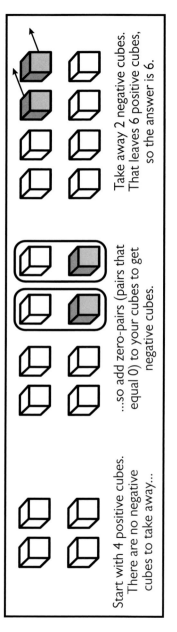

Start with 4 positive cubes. There are no negative cubes to take away...

...so add zero-pairs (pairs that equal 0) to your cubes to get negative cubes.

Take away 2 negative cubes. That leaves 6 positive cubes, so the answer is 6.

Subtraction Puzzles

To find the answer for each square, start with the number in the left column and subtract the number in the top row.

This example shows 0 − 4 = −4:

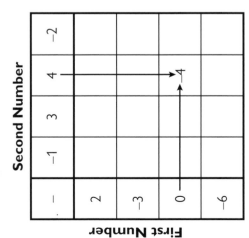

−	−1	3	4	−2
2				
−3				
0			−4	
−6				

Second Number (top row) • First Number (left column)

Puzzle 1

Find the missing value for each square and fill it in.

−	−1	5	4	−2
2				
−3				
0				
−6				

Second Number (top row) • First Number (left column)

Puzzle 2

Find *all* the missing values and fill them in.

−	−5	9	6	
4				
−9			−1	
	−3			
				15

Second Number (top row) • First Number (left column)

MAKING MATHEMATICAL ARGUMENTS
© Creative Publications • MathScape

Multiplication with Signed Numbers

Positive × Positive This shows +6. A positive number times a positive number always has a positive result.	**Case 1** 2 × 3 can be shown as 2 groups of 3. 
Positive × Negative This shows −6. A positive number times a negative number will result in a negative number.	**Case 2** 2 × (−3) means 2 groups of −3. 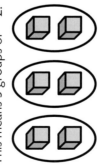
Negative × Positive This shows −6 also. A negative number times a positive number will result in a negative number.	**Case 3** −2 × 3 means −2 groups of 3. However, we cannot readily depict a negative number of groups. −2 × 3 is really the same as 3 × (−2). This means 3 groups of −2.
Negative × Negative A negative number times a negative number will result in a positive number. −2 × (−3) = +6	**Case 4** −2 × (−3) should mean −2 groups of −3. Again, we cannot readily depict a negative number of groups. Consider instead the following pattern: 2 × (−3) = −6 1 × (−3) = −3 0 × (−3) = 0 Continuing the pattern of adding 3 to each product: −1 × (−3) = 3 −2 × (−3) = 6

Investigating Squares of Fractions

Why is the square of a fraction smaller than the original fraction?

Look at the following example in which $\frac{1}{4}$ is the original fraction and $\frac{1}{16}$ is the square of that fraction.

$$\left(\frac{1}{4}\right)^2 = \frac{1}{4} \times \frac{1}{4} = \frac{1}{16}$$

Use a tool, such as cubes or sketches, to show why this rule is true: "The square of a fraction is smaller than the original fraction." Follow these steps:

1. Choose an easy fraction and show that fraction using your tool.

2. When you first learned to multiply, you learned that 2×4 means 2 groups of 4. Show the following using your tool and include a drawing.

   a. $2 \times \frac{1}{4}$ means 2 groups of $\frac{1}{4}$.

   b. $\frac{1}{2} \times \frac{1}{4}$ means half a group of $\frac{1}{4}$.

   c. $\frac{1}{4} \times \frac{1}{2}$ means a fourth of a group of $\frac{1}{2}$.

3. Try different examples of a fraction squared. How can you use your tool to show that the square of the fraction will be smaller than the original fraction?

4. Why is the square of a fraction smaller than the original fraction? Write an explanation to show how your method works. Use pictures in your explanation. Show your method to someone else and teach him or her how to use your model.

Guidelines for Writing Your Own Mathematical Argument

Write your own mathematical argument about the rule you found. Use the different points below as a checklist to make sure you have included all the necessary information to make your argument a strong one.

1. What is your rule?

- Did you state your rule clearly?

- Could someone who had not already done the problem understand your rule?

- Did you describe your rule generally so that it can apply to more than just a few numbers?

2. How did you figure out your rule?

- What methods did you use to figure out your rule?

- What counterexamples did you find where your rule did not work?

3. What special cases does your rule apply to?

- Does your rule work for 0? for 1? for fractions? for negative numbers?

- Are there other cases for which your rule works or does not work?

- If your rule does not work for some cases, explain why it doesn't.

GUIDELINES FOR WRITING YOUR OWN MATHEMATICAL ARGUMENT

Centimeter Grid Paper

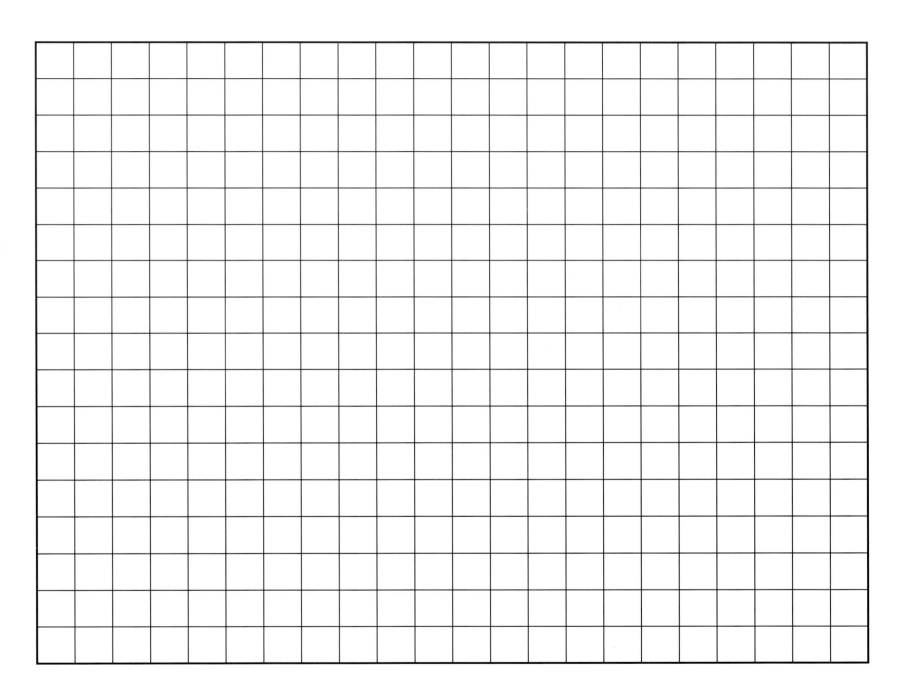

The Bubble Gum Factory Script

Supervisor: (*speaking into the telephone*) Yes, ma'am, we can make bubble gum in 22-inch lengths for your daughter's party. In fact, we can make it in any length you'd like from 1 inch to 100 inches. We just put any of our 1-inch starter pieces into the appropriate stretching machine, and it comes out stretched to the length you order. (*pauses*) Certainly, 20 boxes of 22-inch bubble gum to be picked up tomorrow. Thank you very much. (*hangs up*) Great! That's my largest order today! I'll go check with the people on machine 22 and get them on it right away.

(*Supervisor goes over to machine 22, to talk to Employee 1 and Employee 2*)

Employee 1: (*to supervisor*) Hello! What good timing! We were just going to come see you. Good old 22 has broken down just this morning, so we're going to have to call in a mechanic to see what the trouble is.

(*Supervisor looks upset.*)

Employee 2: (*to supervisor*) What's the matter?

Supervisor: Oh no! This is awful! I just got our largest order today for 22-inch bubble gum and now you tell me the machine is broken! This machine has *never* broken down before! Why did it have to be today?

Employee 1: Listen, I'll try to go get the mechanic myself. Maybe we can get her up here right away and she can have 22 up and running again in no time.

Employee 2: Actually, I don't think we need the mechanic.

Supervisor: (*astonished*) What!?

Employee 2: No, we don't need her. We can just take a 1-inch starter piece and put it through machine 2 to stretch it to twice its length. Then we can put the new piece through machine 11 to stretch it to eleven times its length. Then it will be 22 inches. We don't even need machine 22!

Supervisor: What a great idea! Why didn't I think of that? (*to employee 2*) You deserve a nice big bonus for saving the day. How would you like an extra case of bubble gum to take home with you?

Employee 2: (*looks rather sick at the suggestion*) Frankly, I'm a little tired of...

Supervisor: (*ignores Employee 2*) I'll have a large case sent down to you at the end of the day. (*walks off, pleased.*) Imagine that! Machines 2 and 11. What a marvelous idea!

Employee 1: (*to Employee 2*) That's an interesting idea you had. What other machines in this place do you think we could do without?

The Unnecessary Machines

1	2	3	4	5	6	7	8	9	10
11	12	13	14	15	16	17	18	19	20
21	22	23	24	25	26	27	28	29	30
31	32	33	34	35	36	37	38	39	40
41	42	43	44	45	46	47	48	49	50
51	52	53	54	55	56	57	58	59	60
61	62	63	64	65	66	67	68	69	70
71	72	73	74	75	76	77	78	79	80
81	82	83	84	85	86	87	88	89	90
91	92	93	94	95	96	97	98	99	100

Multiplication Chart

×	1	2	3	4	5	6	7	8	9	10	11	12	13	14	15	16	17	18	19	20
1	1	2	3	4	5	6	7	8	9	10	11	12	13	14	15	16	17	18	19	20
2	2	4	6	8	10	12	14	16	18	20	22	24	26	28	30	32	34	36	38	40
3	3	6	9	12	15	18	21	24	27	30	33	36	39	42	45	48	51	54	57	60
4	4	8	12	16	20	24	28	32	36	40	44	48	52	56	60	64	68	72	76	80
5	5	10	15	20	25	30	35	40	45	50	55	60	65	70	75	80	85	90	95	100
6	6	12	18	24	30	36	42	48	54	60	66	72	78	84	90	96	102	108	114	120
7	7	14	21	28	35	42	49	56	63	70	77	84	91	98	105	112	119	126	133	140
8	8	16	24	32	40	48	56	64	72	80	88	96	104	112	120	128	136	144	152	160
9	9	18	27	36	45	54	63	72	81	90	99	108	117	126	135	144	153	162	171	180
10	10	20	30	40	50	60	70	80	90	100	110	120	130	140	150	160	170	180	190	200
11	11	22	33	44	55	66	77	88	99	110	121	132	143	154	165	176	187	198	209	220
12	12	24	36	48	60	72	84	96	108	120	132	144	156	168	180	192	204	216	228	240
13	13	26	39	52	65	78	91	104	117	130	143	156	169	182	195	208	221	234	247	260
14	14	28	42	56	70	84	98	112	126	140	154	168	182	196	210	224	238	252	266	280
15	15	30	45	60	75	90	105	120	135	150	165	180	195	210	225	240	255	270	285	300

INDEX

MATHSCAPE ACRONYMS AND UNIT TITLES

BB
Buyer Beware

CE
Chance Encounters

FTGU
From the Ground Up

GDTB
Getting Down to Business

GIS
Getting In Shape

LOA
The Language of Algebra

MMA
Making Mathematical Arguments

**MATHSCAPE
ACRONYMS
AND
UNIT TITLES**

BB
Buyer Beware

CE
Chance Encounters

FTGU
From the Ground Up

GDTB
Getting Down to
Business

GIS
Getting In Shape

LOA
The Language of
Algebra

MMA
Making Mathematical
Arguments